KATE GREENAWAY

331. Watercolor. 34.5 x 23.0 cm. Signed "K.G."

AA

KATE GREENAWAY

A Catalogue of the Kate Greenaway Collection
Rare Book Room, Detroit Public Library

compiled by Susan Ruth Thomson

*Published by Wayne State University Press
for the Friends of the Detroit Public Library
Detroit 1977*

Library of Congress Cataloging in Publication Data

Detroit. Public Library.
    Kate Greenaway: a catalogue of the Kate Greenaway Collection, Rare Book Room, Detroit Public Library.

    Includes index.
    1. Greenaway, Kate, 1846-1901 — Bibliography.
2. Detroit. Public Library. I. Thomson, Susan Ruth, 1941 —
Z8368.985.D42 1977   [NC978.5.G7]   016.741'092'4
ISBN 0-8143-1581-X   77-5222

CONTENTS

FOREWORD

In 1959 the Friends of the Detroit Public Library published as their Christmas Keepsake an exhibit catalogue of the John S. Newberry Gift Collection of Kate Greenaway, which had been presented to the Rare Book Room. Kate Greenaway was a British book illustrator who delighted the children of many nations during the last three decades of the 1800s and well into the twentieth century. She ranked in popularity with two of her contemporaries, Randolph Caldecott and Walter Crane, and the trio, aided by the gifted engraver, Edmund Evans, made a great impact on nineteenth-century book illustration. Mr. Newberry continued to add to the collection until his death in 1964, when the Library lost a great benefactor.

The importance of the already substantial Kate Greenaway holdings was recognized by the Friends, so the organization took upon itself the task of providing the financial support necessary to augment the collection when significant material came to light. In 1970 we were able to make a major purchase from the estate of Robert Partridge, a British collector, adding new titles, variant editions, elusive ephemera, and the correspondence to Marion Harry Spielmann pertaining to his biography of Miss Greenaway.

In addition to the generosity of the Friends, many individuals have donated books from their own collections or money to buy available items. To these individuals we extend our heartfelt appreciation: Mr. and Mrs. Joseph Barta, Dr. and Mrs. Ned I. Chalat, Mr. and Mrs. Glenn M. Coulter, one "Miss Curtis," James C. Dance, June Eckmeter, Charles E. Feinberg, Mr. and Mrs. George Garner, Mr. G. W. Gillis, Mrs. Elizabeth Halfert, Mrs. Frank J. Hecker, Thekla Hodgson, Mrs. Austin G. Melcher, F. L. Scharlach, Mrs. George E. Schott, Mrs. William M. Swan, Walter Thomson, Jess Toth, Trinity Circle, and Mr. and Mrs. William Vance.

This catalogue, compiled by Susan Ruth Thomson, who has helped the collection grow to its present size through her acumen, knowledge, and persistence, has been several years in the making. It is not intended to be a definitive bibliography, but we hope it will prove a useful source for Kate Greenaway fans and collectors by bringing together in one checklist bits of information widely scattered.

Gloria A. Francis, *Curator, Rare Book Room*

PREFACE

For purposes of this catalogue the material in the Kate Greenaway collection has been divided into four major categories: books containing her illustrations; magazines and annuals containing her illustrations; calendars, cards, invitations, programs, etc., containing her illustrations; and original Kate Greenaway material, including drawings and letters. Following the drawings and letters is a small collection of her awards and a bibliography of material concerning her life and work selected from the collection. A short introduction explains the form of entry in each category. The catalogue entry number and other pertinent information are found under each illustration.

Dates have not been assigned to the material in this catalogue. However, every attempt has been made to indicate dates when they appear. Dated signatures of individuals, copyright information, publisher's codes, etc., are all noted. A chronological "List of Books, etc., Illustrated Wholly or in Part by Kate Greenaway" appears at the end of H. M. Spielmann and G. S. Layard's *Kate Greenaway* (London, 1905). In addition to this listing, the following information on publishers of K.G. material should prove useful: about 1885 Griffith & Farran became Griffith, Farran, Okeden & Welsh, and about 1897 the firm became Griffith, Farran, Browne & Company Limited. Marcus Ward & Co. became Marcus Ward & Co. Limited about 1890. In 1901 Frederick Warne & Co. became the holders of the copyright work of K.G. originally issued by George Routledge & Sons, and sometime between 1918 and 1920 the firm added Ltd. to its name.

32. *Kate Greenaway's Album,* one of eight copies printed; the book was never published.

47*c*. Presentation copy with watercolor drawing.

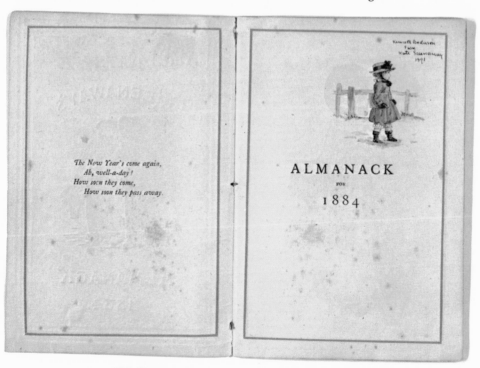

48*d*. Presentation copy with watercolor drawing.

K.G

108. Watercolor studies from a dummy copy of *The Queen of the Pirate Isle*.

334. Chalk drawing. 32.8 x 24.4 cm.

The Green Wave

Those long Green waves — that creep along the Shore
Would they Curled over me — For Evermore
And mermaids danced — to the tumultous roar

There I would lie — and think How Grand
The Sunset lay upon the Yellow Sand
And Count the Scattered sea shells on the Strand

There might I lie and listen to hear
All the wild waters — From Far and near
Sing to each other in the evening Clear —

There might I see — a little water Sprite
Chasing the Sea Horsed Crabs — with glad delight
And Star Fish Glittering in the glorious night —

And Still as I lay there — after a time
A large Pale golden Moon — would rise and Shine
Up to the Silver Stars — and all is mine

All in that wonderful — pale Heaven of Blue
So deep and Fathomless — to I —— To You
Think — if One only — Half the Mystery Knew

I laid me Here For this. I had a Soul to save
And well it is with me — that I was brave
And took this lovely white Frothed watery Grave

And onward Come the Green waves — Crash — and Fall
And the Gay dancing water Sprites — they sing and call
Oh is not this Far better —— best of all .

335. Watercolor. 6.4 x 12.5 cm. Poem in the hand of K.G.

336. Watercolor. 16.8 x 25.4 cm.

358. Watercolor. 16.5 x 28.8 cm.

14

360. Self-portrait. Watercolor. 14.5 x 10.8 cm.

BOOKS

The wording on the title page of each book has been copied exactly as it appears, with capitals, small letters, punctuation, and line endings shown. Typefaces, large and small capitals, printer's ornaments, illustrations, etc., are not included. If more than one book has the same wording on the title page, each one is listed under the main entry as *a*, *b*, *c*, etc. When there is any variation in the wording on the title page, a new entry is begun.

For most of the books the paging is the next item given unless two or more books have the same title page but different paging. In that case the paging for each book is indicated. Page numbers are given as they appear in the book. Those that are supplied by the compiler are enclosed in brackets. For example, [v] vi–[x] 11–192 [1] 2–[8] p. should be read as follows: the first five pages are unnumbered, page 6 is numbered in Roman numerals but page 10 is not numbered; page 11 is numbered in Arabic numerals, and the paging continues, numbered or not, to page 192, which is numbered; after page 192 there are an additional eight pages, page 1 not numbered, page 2 numbered in Arabic, and page 8 not numbered. For two sets of preliminary pages, one numbered and one both unnumbered and numbered, different numerals are used. For example, [4] [ii] iii–x means that the first numbered page in the book is page iii, pages i–ii are unnumbered, and there are also four unnumbered pages before page i. After the pagination, the height of the page is given in centimeters.

The description of the binding is next. It begins with a general statement followed by a description of the front cover, spine, and back cover. The wording on the binding is indicated following the same procedure used for the wording on the title page. Included in the binding description are the edges of the book, if necessary, and the endpapers.

Next, peculiarities of the book are given, such as dust jacket, printing information, copyright notices, advertisements, inscriptions when dated, bookplates, etc. This is followed by a listing of the illustrations done by Kate Greenaway only if her name does not appear on the title page or if the work contains illustrations by more than one artist.

When more than one book is described under the same entry, such as 12*a*, *b*, *c*, etc., the information preceding *a* pertains to all the copies in the entry.

1. ALBUM [Blank book. n.p., n.d.]
   a. [58] 1. Oblong. 10.2 x 17.0 cm.
   Blue cloth. *Front cover:* picture of mother and son watching a goose chase a dog away from her young, stamped in colors. *Spine:* decorative, stamped in black. *Back cover:* ribbon motif, blind-stamped. Rounded corners. All edges stained silver. Imitation white watered silk endpapers.
   Inscription dated "Christmas 1881," verso of front flyleaf.
   Contains unsigned colored illustrations by K.G., ll. [1, 6, 15, 33, 42, and 53].
   Presented by the Friends of the Detroit Public Library.

   b. [59] 1. Oblong. 11.8 x 19.0 cm.
   Yellow cloth. *Front cover:* picture of boy and girl in a cart being pulled by a goat, with two boys and two dogs looking on, stamped in colors. *Spine:* decorative, stamped in black. *Back cover:* ribbon motif, blind-stamped. Rounded corners. All edges stained silver. Imitation white watered silk endpapers.
   Signature dated "Jan. 4th 1885 Wyoming Luzerno County Penna.," l. [32].
   Contains unsigned colored illustrations by K.G., ll. [1, 8, 26, 35, 44, and 53].
   Presented by the Friends of the Detroit Public Library.

2.* ALBUM [Blank book. n.p., n.d.]
   [36] l. Oblong. 6.8 x 10.4 cm.
   Yellow cloth. *Front cover:* picture of girl and boy being chased by a dog; the boy has fallen and the dog has snatched his hat, stamped in colors. *Spine:* decorative, stamped in black. *Back cover:* ribbon motif, blind-stamped. Rounded corners. All edges stained silver. Leaves [1] and [36] used as pastedowns.
   Signature dated "Dec. 12 '83," l. [7].
   Contains unsigned colored illustrations by K.G., ll. [3, 9, 14, 19, 23, and 29] (these illustrations are different from those in item 1).
   Presented by the Friends of the Detroit Public Library.

3. Allingham, William
   RHYMES | FOR THE | YOUNG FOLK | BY | WILLIAM AL-LINGHAM | WITH PICTURES BY | HELEN ALLINGHAM, KATE GREENAWAY, | CAROLINE PATERSON, AND HARRY FURNISS | ENGRAVED AND PRINTED BY EDMUND EVANS | CASSELL AND COMPANY, LIMITED, | LONDON, PARIS,

*Illustrated.

2. Title page from a late nineteenth-century autograph album.

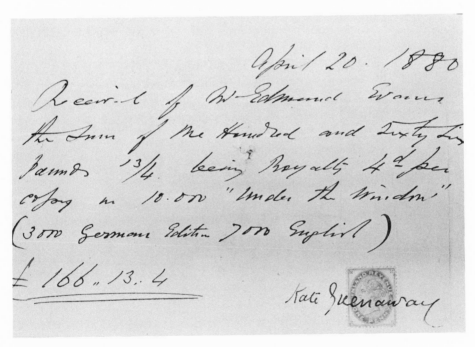

70. Receipt to Edmund Evans for royalties on *Under the Window*.

NEW YORK AND MELBOURNE

[14] 15–75 [76] [16] p. 20.9 cm.

Orange glazed pictorial boards. *Front cover:* Rhymes | for the | Young Folk | By | WILLIAM | ALLINGHAM, printed in black and white; picture of seated mother caressing a child, signed "H.A.," and branches, printed in colors. *Spine:* orange cloth. *Back cover:* vase with flowers, printed in black. All edges stained red. Black endpapers.

"Selections from Cassell & Company's Publications," pp. [1–16] at end ("11 G.8.86.," bottom of p. [1]; "11 B.8.86.," bottom of p. [9]).

Presentation inscription: "Henny Allingham with Mama's Love. Dec. 24, 1890," p. [1] at beginning.

Contains a colored illustration signed "K.G.," p. [63], and an unsigned brown-and-white illustration by K.G., p. 67.

Presented by the Friends of the Detroit Public Library.

4.   American Type Founders Company
KATE   GREENAWAYS | MIGNONETTES | PATENT APPLIED FOR AND COPYRIGHTED 1897 BY AMERICAN TYPE FOUNDERS CO.

[20] p. including covers. 15.8 cm.

Light green paper wrappers. *Front cover:* KATE GREEN-AWAYS | MIGNONETTES | PATENT APPLIED FOR AND COPYRIGHTED 1897 BY AMERICAN TYPE FOUNDERS CO., printed in brown; unsigned illustration by K.G. of circular procession of boys and girls surrounding the company's device, printed in white and brown. *Spine:* blank. *Back cover:* same as front cover.

Title taken from cover.

"Branches and Selling Agencies of the American Type Founders Company," verso of front cover.

A trade catalogue of available printer's ornaments.

Presented by the Friends of the Detroit Public Library.

5.   AROUND THE HOUSE | STORIES AND POEMS | WITH ILLUSTRATIONS | BY | KATE GREENAWAY | NEW YORK | WORTHINGTON CO., 747 BROADWAY | 1888

[4] 5–96 p. 23.8 cm.

Glazed pictorial boards. *Front cover:* AROUND THE | HOUSE | NEW YORK R WORTHINGTON, printed in red, brown, and white; diagonally divided picture of boy and girl in front of a fireplace in the upper half and title and palm tree in lower half, printed in colors. *Spine:* dark green line running the length of the book. *Back cover:* same as front cover. White endpapers.

"Copyright, 1888, by R. Worthington," p. [4].

Illustrated title page and frontispiece printed in brown. Outer forms throughout printed in black, inner forms in brown.

A reprint of *Chatterbox Hall* (item 21) with slight variations.

Presented by the Friends of the Detroit Public Library.

6.   ART IN THE NURSERY. | PICTURES FOR BABY TO DRAW. | AND | PICTURES FOR BABY TO LAUGH AT. | BOSTON: | D. LOTHROP & CO., PUBLISHERS, | 30 & 32 FRANKLIN STREET.

[32] p. Oblong. 12.1 x 18.9 cm.

Gray pictorial boards. *Front cover:* ART IN THE NURSERY. | D. LOTHROP & CO. | BOSTON. | J. H. BUFFORD'S SONS LITH. BOSTON, printed in black; unsigned picture by K.G. of several children painting, printed in colors. *Spine:* green cloth. *Back cover:* publisher's advertisement for "A Magnificent Library of Gift Books," printed in brown. White endpapers.

"Copyright, 1879, By D. Lothrop & Co." and "John Wilson & Son. University Press," p. [4].

7.   AUNT LOUISA'S | CHARMS FOR CHILDREN: | COMPRIS-ING | PUMPKIN HOUSE, DIAMONDS AND TOADS, | SLEEP-ING BEAUTY, BOB'S SCHOOL DAYS. | WITH | TWENTY-FOUR PAGES OF ILLUSTRATIONS. | PRINTED IN COLORS. | MCLOUGHLIN BROS., NEW YORK.

[110] p. 26.5 cm.

Red cloth, beveled edges. *Front cover:* AUNT LOUISA'S | CHARMS FOR CHILDREN, stamped in gold and red; picture of the fainting princess from "Sleeping Beauty," printed in colors on glazed paper, pasted in the center; decorative border, stamped in black and gold. *Spine:* CHARMS FOR CHILDREN, enclosed in decorative design, stamped in gold. *Back cover:* same as front cover, without illustration, blind-stamped. All edges stained red. White endpapers.

Contains six unsigned colored illustrations by K.G. for "Diamonds and Toads," pp. [60–81] (these illustrations are re-engraved from those in "Diamonds and Toads" in *Aunt Louisa's Nursery Favourite*, item 8).

Presented by the Friends of the Detroit Public Library.

8.   AUNT LOUISA'S | NURSERY FAVOURITE. | COMPRISING | Diamonds and Toads. Lily Sweetbriar. | Dick Whittington. Uncle's Farm Yard. | WITH | TWENTY-FOUR PAGES OF ILLUS-TRATIONS. | Printed in Colours by Kronheim. | LONDON: | FREDERICK WARNE AND CO. | BEDFORD STREET, COV-

ENT GARDEN. | NEW YORK: SCRIBNER, WELFORD AND CO. | 1870

[xi] 1–6, 1–[6], 1–6, 1–6 p. (i.e., 154 p.; only text pages numbered). 26.5 cm.

Dark red cloth. *Front cover:* AUNT LOUISA'S | NURSERY FAVOURITE | COLOURED ILLUSTRATIONS, enclosed in decorative design, stamped in gold; inner decorative border, blind-stamped; outer decorative border, stamped in gold. *Spine:* AUNT LOUISA'S NURSERY FAVOURITE, enclosed in decorative border, stamped in gold. *Back cover:* decorative inner border and four-line outer border, blind-stamped. Cream-colored endpapers.

Signature dated "December 30th 1871," p. [1].

Contains six unsigned colored illustrations by K.G. for "Diamonds and Toads." ("Amongst the early and unsigned work [of K.G.] done for Messrs. Kronheim, who had a great colour-printing establishment in Shoe Lane, may be mentioned *Diamonds and Toads,* in 'Aunt Louisa's London Toy Books' Series ((published by Frederick Warne and Co.)), containing six full-page unsigned drawings" [M. H. Spielmann and G. S. Layard, *Kate Greenaway* (London, 1905), p. 49.])

Presented by the Friends of the Detroit Public Library.

9.   Barry, Fanny

Soap-Bubble | Stories. | FOR CHILDREN. | BY | FANNY BARRY, | AUTHOR OF "THE FOX FAMILY," "THE OBSTINATE ELM LEAF," "THE BEARS | OF WUNDERMERK," ETC. | Second Edition. | London: | SKEFFINGTON & SON, 163 PICCADILLY, W. | 1892.

[4] [i]-x, [1] 2–214 p. 17.5 cm.

Blue-speckled cloth. *Front cover:* SOAP | BUBBLE | STORIES, stamped in blue and white; picture of three elves blowing bubbles, each bubble containing the title of one of the stories in the book, stamped in blue and white. *Spine:* SOAP- | BUBBLE | STORIES | SKEFFINGTON'S, stamped in blue; picture of elf and bubbles, stamped in blue and white. *Back cover:* blank. All edges stained yellow. Green floral endpapers.

Contains one black-and-white illustration signed "K.G.," p. 162.

Presented by the Friends of the Detroit Public Library.

10.   BIB AND TUCKER FOLKS | WITH | PICTURES AND STORIES FOR LITTLE PEOPLE | IN THE NURSERY | BOSTON | D. LOTHROP AND COMPANY | FRANKLIN AND HAWLEY STREETS

[192] p. 23.0 cm.

Glazed pictorial boards. *Front cover:* BIB AND TUCKER FOLKS | H. BENCKE, LITH. N.Y., printed in black; picture of two children surrounded by flowers and vines, printed in colors. *Spine:* BIB | AND | TUCKER | FOLKS, printed in black; flowers, printed in colors. *Back cover:* picture of young boy kissing girl on the cheek and several children being pulled on a sled by a pair of ice skaters, printed in colors. White endpapers.

"Copyright, 1886, by D. Lothrop & Company," p. [4].

Inscription dated "Christmas 1886," p. [1].

Contains five unsigned black-and-white illustrations by K.G., pp. [20, 21, 87, and 169], and one black-and-white illustration signed "K.G.," p. [120].

Presented by the Friends of the Detroit Public Library.

11. Blood, Gertrude

TOPO | A Tale about English Children in Italy | BY | G. E. BRUNEFILLE | WITH 44 PEN-AND-INK ILLUSTRATIONS | BY KATE GREENAWAY | London: | MARCUS WARD & CO., 67 and 68, CHANDOS STREET | AND ROYAL ULSTER WORKS, BELFAST | 1878.

a. [7] 8–140 [141–42] [1] 2–25 [26] p. 16.8 cm.

Green cloth, beveled edges. *Front cover:* TOPO | BY G. E. BRUNEFILLE | ILLUSTRATED BY KATE GREENWAY, stamped in gold and black; picture of young girl pulling a small cart with doll, in front of a balustrade, stamped in black and gold. *Spine:* TOPO | MARCUS WARD & CO., stamped in gold and black; picture of young girl picking apples, stamped in black and gold. *Back cover:* double-line border, blind-stamped. All edges gilt. Brown endpapers. Thickness of volume excluding covers: 1.7 cm.

Frontispiece inserted. "Marcus Ward & Co., London and Belfast" at bottom of frontispiece.

"Marcus Ward & Co., Royal Ulster Works, Belfast," p. 140.

"A Catalogue of Marcus Ward and Co.'s Publications," pp. [1] 2–25 [26] at end.

Presented by John S. Newberry.

b. [7] 8–140 [1–4] p. 16.9 cm.

Green cloth. *Front cover:* same as item 11a. *Spine:* same as item 11a. *Back cover:* triple-line border, blind-stamped. White endpapers. Thickness of volume, excluding covers: 1.2 cm.

Frontispiece inserted.

"Marcus Ward & Co., Royal Ulster Works, Belfast," p. 140.

Advertisements of "Marcus Ward & Co., London, Belfast, &

Philadelphia," pp. [1–4] at end.
From the collection of Robert Partridge.
Presented by the Friends of the Detroit Public Library.

12.   Boutell, Mary Elizabeth Chevallier
TWO LITTLE COUSINS | BY | ALICE HEPBURN | London: | MARCUS WARD & CO., 67, CHANDOS STREET | AND ROYAL ULSTER WORKS, BELFAST | 1876
[9] 10–159 [160] p. 13.9 cm.
Green cloth. *Front cover:* TWO | LITTLE COUSINS, stamped in gold; floral design forms right and bottom border, stamped in black; picture of two children and a lamb, printed in colors on glazed paper, pasted in upper left-hand corner. *Spine:* TWO | LITTLE | COUSINS | MARCUS WARD & CO., stamped in gold and black; decorative design stamped in black. *Back cover:* double-line border, blind-stamped. Cream-colored endpapers.
"Marcus Ward & Co., Royal Ulster Works, Belfast," p. 159.
Contains four unsigned colored illustrations by K.G., printed on stiff paper and mounted within a gold border, inserted as frontispiece and after pp. 34, 72, and 152.
Copy imperfect, lacking pp. 15–16, 65–66, 69–76, and 79–80, including one illustration, "Six Happy Little Girls," after p. 72.

13.   Briggs & Co.
BRIGGS & CO'S | Patent | Transferring Papers. | Protected by | Her most Gracious Majesty's | Royal Letters Patent. | A WARM IRON PASSED OVER | THE BACK OF THESE PAPERS | TRANSFERS THE PATTERN TO | ANY FABRIC. | Sole Inventors and Patentees | BRIGGS & CO. | MANCHESTER.
[6] 7–182 p. 21.4 cm.
Brown cloth. *Front cover:* BRIGGS' PATENT, stamped in gold; corner design of flowers and double-line border, blind-stamped. *Spine:* blank. *Back cover:* corner design and double-line border, same as front cover, blind-stamped. White endpapers.
"Village Scenes. By Kate Greenaway," pp. 104–9; other patterns after K.G., pp. 145–46.
Copy imperfect, lacking pp. 11–12, 19–20, 33–34, 77–78, and 155–56.
Presented by John S. Newberry.

14.   Brine, Mary D.
CHRISTMAS DREAMS | BY | MARY D. BRINE | AUTHOR OF "THE MERRY GO-ROUND," "JINGLES AND JOYS," "PA-PA'S LITTLE | DAUGHTERS SERIES," "STORIES GRANDMA TOLD," ETC., ETC. | CASSELL & COMPANY, LIMITED, | 739

& 741 BROADWAY, NEW YORK.

[48] p. 27.0 cm.

Glazed pictorial boards. *Front cover:* christmas | DREAMS | CASSELL & COMPANY LIMITED | NEW YORK LONDON PARIS & MELBOURNE COPYRIGHT 1886 | BY O. M. DUNHAM, printed in blue, red, and black; picture of young girl in rocking chair dreaming of Christmas, surrounded by flowers, printed in colors. *Spine:* rebacked. *Back cover:* picture of birds and flowers, printed in colors. White endpapers.

"Copyright, 1886, by O. M. Dunham" and "Press of W. L. Mershon & Co., Rahway, N.J.," p. [4].

Inscription dated "Christmas 1886," recto front flyleaf.

Contains four black-and-white illustrations signed "K.G.," pp. [15, 19, 28, and 30], and one unsigned black-and-white illustration by K.G., p. [30].

Presented by Mrs. William M. Swan.

15. Brown, Emma E.
ONCE UPON A TIME. | PLAY-STORIES FOR CHILDREN. | BY | EMMA E. BROWN. | BOSTON: | D. LOTHROP AND COMPANY, | FRANKLIN ST., CORNER OF HAWLEY.

[4] 5–274 [2] p. 17.0 cm.

Glazed pictorial boards. *Front cover:* ONCE UPON A TIME. | D. LOTHROP & CO. BOSTON, printed in black; picture of two boys ringing a bell, girl playing with toys, and a church, printed in colors. *Spine:* green cloth with ONCE UPON | A TIME | D. LOTHROP stamped in gold; decorative design, stamped in black and gold. *Back cover:* advertisement for *Papa's Boy* with picture of mother hugging a child, printed in brown. White endpapers.

"Copyright, 1879, By D. Lothrop & Co." and "Wright & Potter Printing Company, 79 Milk Street, Boston.," p. [4].

Advertisement for *Six Little Rebels* by Kate Tannatt Woods and *The Dogberry Bunch* by Mary Hartwell Catherwood, pp. [1–2] at end.

Contains two black-and-white illustrations signed "K.G.," pp. 19 and 106, and one unsigned black-and-white illustration by K.G., p. 244.

16. Browning, Robert
ROBERT BROWNING | L'Homme à la Flûte | INTERPRÉTA-TION DE J. GIRARDIN | ILLUSTRATIONS | DE | KATE GREENAWAY | PARIS | LIBRAIRIE HACHETTE ET CIE | 79, BOULEVARD SAINT-GERMAIN 79 | 1889

[4] 5–64 p. 25.0 cm.

Light brown glazed boards. *Front cover:* Robert Browning | L'Homme à la Flûte | Interprétation | de J. Girardin | ILLUS-TRATIONS | DE | KATE GREENAWAY, printed in black and white; illustration of Pied Piper, printed in colors. *Spine:* brown cloth. *Back cover:* printer's device, printed in white. All edges stained turquoise. Turquoise endpapers.

"Gravé et Imprimé par Edmond Evans, Racquet Court, Fleet Street, Londres," p. [4].

Presented by John S. Newberry.

17. Browning, Robert
THE PIED PIPER | OF | HAMELIN | BY | ROBERT BROWN-ING | WITH 35 ILLUSTRATIONS | BY | KATE GREENAWAY | ENGRAVED AND PRINTED IN COLOURS BY EDMUND EVANS | LONDON | GEORGE ROUTLEDGE AND SONS | BROADWAY, LUDGATE HILL | GLASGOW, MANCHESTER AND NEW YORK

a. [4] 5–64 p. 25.0 cm.

Light brown glazed pictorial boards. *Front cover:* The | Pied Piper | of Hamelin | by | Robert Browning. | ILLUSTRATED BY | KATE GREENAWAY, printed in white and black; picture of Pied Piper, printed in colors. *Spine:* brown cloth. *Back cover:* printer's device, printed in white. All edges stained blue. Dark blue endpapers.

"Published by arrangement with the Proprietors of the Copyright," p. [4].

Presented by John S. Newberry.

b. [2] 3–63 [64] p. 25.2 cm.

Pink cloth. *Front cover:* The | Pied Piper | of Hamelin | by | Robert Browning. | ILLUSTRATED BY | KATE GREENAWAY, stamped in gold and brown; picture of Pied Piper, stamped in red and gold. *Spine:* blank. *Back cover:* blank. All edges stained red. Turquoise endpapers.

Pages [19–20] blank, although no text or illustrations are missing.

Presented by the Friends of the Detroit Public Library.

18. Browning, Robert
THE PIED PIPER | OF | HAMELIN | BY | ROBERT BROWN-ING | ILLUSTRATED BY | KATE GREENAWAY | LONDON | FREDERICK WARNE AND CO. | AND NEW YORK

[3] 4–48 p. 24.8 cm.

Dark green glazed pictorial boards. *Front cover:* THE PIED PIPER | OF HAMELIN | BY | ROBERT | BROWNING | Illustrated by Kate Greenaway, printed in yellow; picture of Pied Piper seated, with children dancing around a tree, printed in colors. *Spine:* tan cloth with THE PIED PIPER OF HAMELIN stamped in black. *Back cover:* same as front cover. Illustrated white and light brown endpapers.

"Engraved and Printed by Edmund Evans, Ltd., The Racquet Court Press, London," p. 48.

Presented by the Friends of the Detroit Public Library.

19. Browning, Robert
   THE PIED PIPER | OF | HAMELIN | BY | ROBERT BROWN-ING | ILLUSTRATED BY | KATE GREENAWAY | LONDON | FREDERICK WARNE AND CO., LTD | AND NEW YORK
   [3] 4–48 p. 24.8 cm.
   Dark green glazed pictorial boards. *Front cover:* same as item 18. *Spine:* brown cloth with THE PIED PIPER OF HAMELIN stamped in dark green. *Back cover:* same as front cover. All edges stained yellow. Illustrated white and light brown endpapers.
   "Printed in Great Britain," p. 4.
   "Engraved and Printed by Edmund Evans, Ltd., Rose Place, Globe Road, London, E. I.," p. 48.
   Presented by Mr. G. W. Gillis.

20. BUBBLES | BRIGHT | FOR | PET'S | DELIGHT | MCLOUGHLIN BROS. | NEW YORK.
   [16] p. 24.8 cm.
   Glazed pictorial boards. *Front cover:* BUBBLES | BRIGHT | FOR | PET'S | DELIGHT | MCLOUGHLIN BROS. | NEW YORK | BANNER | SERIES, printed in red, gold, and black; picture of girl riding a bicycle, printed in colors. *Spine:* black cloth. *Back cover:* blank.
   Title taken from cover.
   Contains one black-and-white illustration signed "K.G.," p. [2].

21. CHATTERBOX HALL | ILLUSTRATED BY | KATE GREENAWAY | R WORTHINGTON NEW YORK
   [4] 5–96 p. 24.2 cm.
   Glazed pictorial boards. *Front cover:* CHATTERBOX | HALL | ILLUSTRATED BY KATE GREENAWAY | R WORTHINGTON NEW YORK BEATTY. FORST & DE YONGH LITH 44 W. BROADWAY, N. Y., printed in several colors; picture of several children looking out a window, printed in colors. *Spine:* black cloth. *Back cover:* beige board with advertisement for "R. Worthington's New Juvenile Books." White endpapers.

"Copyright, 1884, by R. Worthington" and "Press of J. J. Little & Co., Nos. 10 to 20 Astor Place, New York," p. [4].

Signature dated "Christmas 1885," recto front flyleaf.

Reprinted with slight variations as *Around the House* (item 5).

Presented by the Friends of the Detroit Public Library.

22.   THE CHILDREN'S | BIRTHDAY BOOK | LONDON | MAR-
CUS WARD & CO., LIMITED | BELFAST & NEW YORK

[100] p. 16.8 cm.

Red cloth. *Front cover:* The | Children's | Birthday Book,
stamped in gold; small decorative device below title, stamped in
gold. *Spine:* single-line border top and bottom, stamped in
black. *Back cover:* blank. All edges gilt. Blue and gold floral
endpapers.

Monogram: "MW & Co Ld," p. [4].

"Printed & Published by Marcus Ward & Co. Limited London
& Belfast New York," p. [100].

Inscription: "Jack 1894," p. [1].

Contains unsigned colored illustrations by K.G., pp. [5, 6, 9,
12, 21, 28, 35, 39, 53, 69, 76, 78, and 93].

Presented by the Friends of the Detroit Public Library.

23.   Clark, Mary Senior

TURNASIDE COTTAGE | BY | MARY SENIOR CLARK | AU-
THOR OF "LOST LEGENDS OF THE NURSERY RHYMES" |
London: | MARCUS WARD & CO., 67, CHANDOS STREET |
NEW YORK: THOMAS NELSON & SONS | 1875

[7] 8–199 [200] [1] 2–24 p. 16.8 cm.

Green cloth. *Front cover:* TURNASIDE COTTAGE | BY MARY
SENIOR CLARK, stamped in gold; decorative design and
double-line border, stamped in black. *Spine:* TURNASIDE |
COTTAGE | MARCUS WARD & CO., stamped in gold and
black; decorative design, stamped in gold and black. *Back cover:*
trellis design with single-line border, blind-stamped. Cream-
colored endpapers.

Colored frontispiece and added title page on conjugate leaves
inserted after p. [2].

"Marcus Ward & Co., Printers, Royal Ulster Works, Belfast,"
p. 199.

Publisher's catalogue, pp. [1]–24 at end.

Contains unsigned colored frontispiece by K.G. and four
black-and-white illustrations signed "K.G." inserted after pp.
32, 58, 112, and 160.

Presented by the Friends of the Detroit Public Library.

24.   Clark, Mary Senior
    TURNASIDE COTTAGE | BY | MARY SENIOR CLARK | AU-
THOR OF "LOST LEGENDS OF THE NURSERY RHYMES" |
NEW EDITION | LONDON: | MARCUS WARD & CO., LIM-
ITED | ORIEL HOUSE, FARRINGDON STREET | AND AT
BELFAST AND NEW YORK
    [7] 8–199 [200] p. 16.8 cm.
    Red cloth. *Front cover:* Turnaside | Cottage | Illustrated by |
Kate Greenaway, stamped in gold and black; unsigned picture
by K.G. of mother reading to a young boy, stamped in gold and
black. *Spine:* TURNASIDE | COTTAGE | by | MARY SENIOR |
CLARK | MARCUS WARD | & CO LIMITED, stamped in black;
unsigned picture by K.G. of boy with a pitchfork, stamped in
black. *Back cover:* double-line border, blind-stamped. Cream-
colored endpapers.
    Colored frontispiece and added title page on conjugate leaves
inserted after p. [2].
    "Marcus Ward & Co., Printer, Royal Ulster Works, Belfast.,"
p. 99.
    Contains four inserted illustrations.
    From the collection of Robert Partridge.
    Presented by the Friends of the Detroit Public Library.

25.   Cresswell, Beatrice F.
    The Royal Progress | OF | KING PEPITO | BY | BEATRICE F.
CRESSWELL | ILLUSTRATED BY | KATE GREENAWAY | EN-
GRAVED AND PRINTED BY EDMUND EVANS | LONDON |
SOCIETY FOR PROMOTING CHRISTIAN KNOWLEDGE, |
NORTHUMBERLAND AVENUE, CHARING CROSS, W.C.; |
43, QUEEN VICTORIA STREET, E.C. | BRIGHTON: 135,
NORTH STREET. | NEW YORK: E. & J B. YOUNG & CO.
    [9] 10–48 p. 20.6 cm.
    Beige pictorial boards. *Front cover:* PRICE ONE SHILLING |
THE ROYAL PROGRESS | OF | KING PEPITO | BY | BEATRICE
F. CRESSWELL | ILLUSTRATED BY | KATE GREENAWAY |
ENGRAVED AND PRINTED BY EDMUND EVANS | LONDON
| SOCIETY FOR PROMOTING CHRISTIAN KNOWLEDGE, |
NORTHUMBERLAND AVENUE, CHARING CROSS, W.C. |
43, QUEEN VICTORIA STREET, E.C. | BRIGHTON: 135,
NORTH STREET. | NEW YORK: E. & J B. YOUNG & CO.,
printed in black; unsigned picture by K.G. of two women with
pitchforks and a small child with animals, printed in colors.
Spine: THE ROYAL PROGRESS OF KING PEPITO, printed in

black. *Back cover:* Advertisements for "Publications by the late Mrs. Ewing." White endpapers.

Presented by John S. Newberry.

26. DOLL'S TEA PARTY | MERRY PLAY TIME | ILLUSTRATED | BOSTON | LOTHROP PUBLISHING COMPANY

[48] p. 24.6 cm.

Glazed pictorial boards. *Front cover:* DOLLS (*sic*) TEA PARTY | SNOW BIRD SERIES | LOTHROP PUBLISHING COMPANY, | BOSTON., printed in red and brown; picture of doll, cat, and dog seated at a table having tea, printed in colors. *Spine:* light green cloth. *Back cover:* poem entitled "Unappreciated." Pages [1–2] and [47–48] used as pastedowns.

"Copyright, 1895, by Lothrop Publishing Company. All rights reserved," p. [4].

Contains unsigned black-and-white illustrations by K.G., pp. [30 and 46].

Presented by Mrs. George E. Schott in memory of George E. Barrett.

27. ELISE | Illustrated | NEW YORK | DODD, MEAD, AND COMPANY | PUBLISHERS [4] 7–46 p. (i.e., 44 p.) 15.2 cm.

Brown cloth. *Front cover:* decorative circular device in center with double-line border, blind-stamped. *Spine:* ELISE | No 17, stamped in gold. *Back cover:* same as front cover. Yellow endpapers.

"Copyright, 1881, By Dodd, Mead, and Company," p. [4].

Contains black-and-white illustrations signed "K.G.," pp. [3] (title page), 15, and 26; unsigned black-and-white illustrations by K.G., pp. 24, 35, 41, and 45.

28. Ellice, Robert, ed.

Songs for the Nursery: | A Collection of | CHILDREN'S POEMS, | Old and New. | EDITED BY ROBERT ELLICE. | With Illustrations by | KATE GREENAWAY, MISS BENNETT, ROBERT BARNES, ETC. | LONDON: W. MACK, 4, PATERNOSTER SQUARE.

[3] 4–128 p. 13.3 cm.

Light blue cloth. *Front cover:* SONGS for | the | NURSERY, stamped in orange and brown; unsigned picture by K.G. of young boy and girl with muff, bordered by vines on left and tree on right, stamped in orange and brown. *Spine:* SONGS | FOR THE | NURSERY, stamped in orange and brown; parrot and seated girl, stamped in brown. *Back cover:* picture of drummer boy and single-line border, stamped in orange and brown. Olive green floral endpapers.

Publisher's advertisements, pp. 127–28.

Contains unsigned black-and-white illustrations by K.G., pp. 18, 27, 46, 55, 66, 72, 76, 79, 103, and 112.

From the collection of Robert Partridge.

Presented by the Friends of the Detroit Public Library.

29.   EVERY GIRL'S | STORIES | BY | GRACE AGUILAR, GERALDINE BUTT, JANE BUTT, | THE COUNTESS D'AUL-NOY, MARIA EDGEWORTH, | "ESMÉ," MADEMOISELLE DE LA FORCE, | E. GOATLEY, MRS. H. R. HAWEIS, | THE RIGHT HON. E. H. KNATCHBULL-HUGESSEN, | MRS. LUXTON, MRS. HENRY MACKARNESS, | MARY RUSSELL MITFORD, L. MYERS | WITH 24 PAGE ILLUSTRATIONS | LONDON | GEORGE ROUTLEDGE AND SONS, LIMITED | BROADWAY, LUDGATE HILL | MANCHESTER AND NEW YORK | 1896.

[viii] [1] 2–501 [502] [2] p. 19.6 cm.

Blue cloth, beveled edges. *Front cover:* EVERY | GIRL'S | STORIES, stamped in gold; picture of four women having tea, stamped in colors. *Spine:* EVERY | GIRL'S | STORIES | ROUTLEDGE, stamped in gold; picture of standing woman, stamped in colors. *Back cover:* blank. All edges gilt. Brown and white floral endpapers.

"Richard Clay & Sons, Limited, London & Bungay," pp. [iv] and [502].

Publisher's advertisements, pp. [1–2] at end.

Inscription dated "Christmas 1895," p. [1].

Contains inserted unsigned colored frontispiece by K.G.

Presented by the Friends of the Detroit Public Library.

30.   Fell, Archie

DUMPY. | BY ARCHIE FELL. | BOSTON: | D. LOTHROP & CO., PUBLISHERS, | FRANKLIN ST., CORNER OF HAWLEY.

[64] p. 11.3 cm.

Brown cloth. *Front cover:* Dumpy, stamped in black; picture of two children feeding birds, stamped in red and black. *Spine:* blank. *Back cover:* blank. Cream-colored endpapers.

"Copyright by D. Lothrop & Co. 1880," p. [4].

Inscription dated "Christmas, 1881," recto front flyleaf.

Contains one unsigned black-and-white illustration by K.G., p. [52].

Presented by Walter Thomson.

31. Foster, Myles B.

A DAY IN A CHILD'S LIFE. | ILLUSTRATED BY | KATE GREENAWAY. | MUSIC BY MYLES B. FOSTER. | (Organist of the Foundling Hospital.) | ENGRAVED AND PRINTED BY EDMUND EVANS. | LONDON: | GEORGE ROUTLEDGE AND SONS, | BROADWAY, LUDGATE HILL. | NEW YORK: 9, LAFAYETTE PLACE. | [Copyright.]

[5] 6–29 [30] p.

"The Publishers thank . . . ," p. [3].

"London: Engraved and Printed by Edmund Evans, Racquet Court, Fleet Street, E.C.," p. [30].

a. 24.3 cm.

Light green glazed pictorial boards, beveled edges. *Front cover:* A DAY IN | A | CHILD'S LIFE, printed in brown; border of six narrow brown rules alternating with five yellow rules; inside border at each corner containing a yellow sunflower. *Spine:* light green cloth. *Back cover:* same as front cover. All edges stained green. Light green endpapers.

b. 24.3 cm.

Light green glazed pictorial boards, beveled edges. *Front cover:* same as item 31*a*. *Spine:* light green cloth. *Back cover:* same as front cover. All edges stained green. Light green endpapers.

Contains the bookplate of Lady Nevill.

Presentation inscription: "Lady Dorothy Nevill from Kate Greenaway. 1882," p. [3].

Manuscript note, verso of front flyleaf: "purchased from Lady Nevill's son."

Tipped in is a three-page holograph letter from K.G. to Lady Nevill dated December 1, 1882, containing a pen-and-ink sketch measuring 12 cm. showing a back view of a small girl holding an open umbrella and carrying a basket.

Presented by John S. Newberry.

c. 24.3 cm.

Light green glazed pictorial boards, beveled edges. *Front cover:* same as item 31*a*. *Spine:* light green cloth. *Back cover:* same as front cover. All edges stained green. Light green endpapers.

White dust wrapper repeating on the front cover the design from the title page, printed in brown.

Presented by John S. Newberry.

d. 24.2 cm.

Gray glazed pictorial boards, beveled edges. *Front cover:* A DAY IN A CHILD'S | LIFE | KATE GREENAWAY, printed in white; trellis-like border and garland of roses surrounding two seated girls, printed in colors. *Spine:* light green cloth. *Back cover:* same as front cover. All edges stained blue. Light green endpapers.

From the collection of Robert Partridge.

Presented by the Friends of the Detroit Public Library.

e. 23.7 cm.

Rebound copy in gold-tooled green morocco. All edges gilt. Marbled endpapers.

Glazed paper covers (same as item 31*a*) removed from original boards and laid in.

Presented by John S. Newberry.

32.* Greenaway, Kate

[KATE GREENAWAY'S | ALBUM | 192 PICTURES IN GOLD FRAMES | ENGRAVED AND PRINTED BY EDMUND EVANS | LONDON | GEORGE ROUTLEDGE & SONS | BROADWAY, LUDGATE HILL | GLASGOW, MANCHESTER AND NEW YORK]

[48] p. 9.1 cm.

Turquoise wrappers. *Front cover:* five illustrations by K.G., printed in colors on a white background, one in each corner in a circular gold frame and one in the center in a rectangular gold frame; white ribbon motif outlined in gold above and below rectangular illustration in center. *Spine:* blank. *Back cover:* same design as front cover except for different illustrations.

Twenty-four unbound leaves loosely inserted in wrappers. Each leaf contains eight illustrations from the *Birthday Book for Children,* printed in colors and surrounded by gold frames.

According to E. Wilfred Evans, of Edmund Evans, Ltd., only eight copies of *Kate Greenaway's Album* were printed. This copy does not contain a title page: the title page information was taken from the copy of Miss M. I. Meacham. The white ribbon motif on the covers of the wrappers appears to be for the title.

From the estate of John Greenaway.

From the collection of Robert Dennis Hilton Smith.

Presented by the Friends of the Detroit Public Library.

33. Greenaway, Kate

A Apple Pie | BY | KATE GREENAWAY | ENGRAVED AND PRINTED BY EDMUND EVANS |LONDON: GEORGE ROUT-LEDGE AND SONS | BROADWAY, LUDGATE HILL | NEW

*Illustrated.

YORK: 9 LAFAYETTE PLACE

[44] p. Oblong. 21.2 x 26.2 cm.

a. Light green glazed pictorial boards. *Front cover:* A | APPLE | PIE | By KATE GREENAWAY, printed in red; picture of four girls, two carrying apples, one bouncing an apple, and one kneeling behind a flour canister holding a rolling pin, top and top three-quarters of sides bordered with apples and leaves, printed in colors. *Spine:* dark red cloth. *Back cover:* cream-colored board, blank. All edges stained red. Dark blue endpapers.

Presented by John S. Newberry.

b. Blue cloth. *Front cover:* A APPLE PIE | by KATE GREEN-AWAY., stamped in gold; picture of woman cutting a pie, with children watching, stamped in red. *Spine:* blank. *Back cover:* picture of woman seated at a table eating a piece of pie, stamped in red. All edges stained red. Royal blue endpapers.

Presented by the Friends of the Detroit Public Library.

34. Greenaway, Kate

ALMANACH | DE | KATE GREENAWAY | POUR | 1883 | PARIS | LIBRAIRIE HACHETTE ET CIE | 79, BOULEVARD SAINT-GERMAIN, 79 | [Droits de reproduction réservés.

[24] p. 9.9 cm.

Yellow glazed pictorial boards. *Front cover:* ALMANACH | DE | KATE GREENAWAY | POUR | 1883, printed in brown; picture of three girls holding hands above title and one girl curtsying below title, all surrounded by a garland of flowers with ribbons above and below, printed in colors; triple-line border, printed in blue. *Spine:* yellow cloth. *Back cover:* same as front cover except back view of girls. All edges stained blue. Turquoise endpapers.

Advertisement for *Le Journal de la Jeunesse,* p. [24].

Presented by John S. Newberry.

35. Greenaway, Kate

ALMANACH | DE | KATE GREENAWAY | POUR | 1884 | PARIS: LIBRAIRIE HACHETTE ET CIE | 79, BOULEVARD SAINT GERMAIN, 79 | [Droits de reproduction réservés.]

[24] p. 13.2 cm.

Glazed pictorial wrappers. *Front cover:* ALMANACH | POUR L'ANNÉE | 1884 1884 | PAR | KATE GREENAWAY, printed in black; picture of boy and girl sitting on a fence looking at the old man in the moon and his dog, surrounded by a garland of roses, printed in colors. *Spine:* blank. *Back cover:* same as front cover. Pages [1–2] and [23–24] used as pastedowns.

"Londres, Imprimé par Edmund Evans, Racquet Ct., Fleet St.," p. [4].

Presented by John S. Newberry.

36. Greenaway, Kate
ALMANACH | DE | KATE GREENAWAY | POUR | 1885 | PARIS | LIBRAIRIE HACHETTE ET CIE | 79, BOULEVARD SAINT-GERMAIN, 79 | [Droits de reproduction réservés.]

[24] p. 10.0 cm.

Cream-colored glazed pictorial boards. *Front cover:* AL-MANACH | DE | KATE GREENAWAY | 1885, printed in black; picture of three young children standing in a row, trellis border top and bottom, printed in colors. *Spine:* yellow cloth. *Back cover:* trellis rectangle in center, surrounded by a trellis border, printed in colors. All edges stained yellow. Light turquoise endpapers.

Presented by John S. Newberry.

37. Greenaway, Kate
ALMANACH | DE | KATE GREENAWAY | POUR | 1886 | Paris | LIBRAIRIE HACHETTE ET CIE. | 79, Boulevard Saint-Germain, 79

[24] p. 9.9 cm.

Olive green glazed pictorial boards. *Front cover:* ALMANACH | DE | KATE GREENAWAY | POUR | 1886, printed in black; picture of two girls, one pointing with an umbrella, printed in colors; single-line border, printed in black. *Spine:* orange cloth. *Back cover:* vase of flowers, printed in colors. All edges stained blue. Bright yellow endpapers.

"Tous Droits Réservés. Londres: Imprimé par Edmund Evans, Racquet-Ct., Fleet-St.," p. [24].

Presented by John S. Newberry.

38. Greenaway, Kate
ALMANACH | DE | KATE GREENAWAY | POUR | 1887 | LIBRAIRIE HACHETTE ET CIE | [Droits de reproduction ré-servés.]

[24] p. Oblong. 7.5 x 10.2 cm.

Cream-colored glazed pictorial boards. *Front cover:* AL-MANACH POUR 1887 | PAR | KATE GREENAWAY, printed in black; picture of four women representing spring, summer, fall, and winter, printed in colors. *Spine:* yellow cloth. *Back cover:* same as front cover. All edges stained light turquoise. Light turquoise endpapers.

Presented by John S. Newberry.

39. Greenaway, Kate

ALMANACH | DE | KATE GREENAWAY | 1888 | HACHETTE ET CIE.

[24] p. 9.8 cm.

Yellow glazed pictorial boards. *Front cover:* ALMANACH | POUR L'ANNÉE 1888 | PAR | KATE GREENAWAY, printed in brown; picture of back view of two women, stairs and rose bushes in background, printed in colors; triple-line border, printed in brown. *Spine:* blue cloth. *Back cover:* same as front cover. All edges stained blue. Dark blue endpapers.

Presented by John S. Newberry.

40. Greenaway, Kate

ALMANACH | DE | KATE GREENAWAY | 1889 | PARIS | LIBRAIRIE HACHETTE ET CIE | 79, BOULEVARD SAINT-GERMAIN, 79

[24] p. 9.9 cm.

Black glazed pictorial boards. *Front cover:* ALMANACH | DE | KATE GREENAWAY | POUR | 1889 | PARIS | LIBRAIRIE HACHETTE ET CIE | 79 BOULEVARD SAINT-GERMAIN 79, printed in white; picture of two women seated at a table having tea, printed in colors. *Spine:* yellow cloth. *Back cover:* picture of three girls dancing, printed in colors. All edges stained red. Red endpapers.

"Gravé et imprimé par E. Evans, Racquet Court, Londres," p. [24].

Presented by John S. Newberry.

41. Greenaway, Kate

ALMANACH | DE | KATE GREENAWAY | 1890 | LIBRAIRIE HACHETTE ET CIE

[24] p. 9.9 cm.

Black glazed pictorial boards. *Front cover:* ALMANACH | DE | KATE GREENAWAY | 1890, printed in white; picture of three small girls, the one in the middle holding a basket of flowers over her head, printed in colors; floral border, printed in colors. *Spine:* red cloth. *Back cover:* girl and boy dancing, printed in colors; floral border, printed in colors. All edges stained red. Red endpapers.

"Gravé et imprimé par E. Evans, Racquet Court, Londres," p. [24].

Presented by John S. Newberry.

42. Greenaway, Kate
ALMANACH | DE | KATE GREENAWAY | POUR | 1891 |
PARIS | LIBRARIE (*sic*) HACHETTE ET CIE | 79, BOULEVARD
SAINT-GERMAIN, 79

[24] p. 10.0 cm.

White glazed pictorial boards. *Front cover:* ALMANACH | DE |
KATE GREENAWAY | POUR | 1891 | PARIS | LIBRAIRIE
HACHETTE ET CIE, printed in blue; picture of woman holding
a child and two small children at each side, printed in colors;
wide leafy border, printed in green. *Spine:* yellow cloth. *Back
cover:* same as front cover except picture is of a young girl holding a garland of flowers, printed in colors. All edges stained
yellow. Turquoise endpapers.

"London, Engraved & Printed at Racquet Court, by Edmund
Evans" and "Gravé et imprimé par E. Evans, Racquet Court,
Londres," p. [24].

Presented by John S. Newberry.

43. Greenaway, Kate
ALMANACH | DE | KATE GREENAWAY | POUR | 1892 |
PARIS: LIBRAIRIE HACHETTE ET CIE.

[24] p. 9.9 cm.

Cream-colored glazed pictorial boards. *Front cover:* AL-
MANACH | DE | KATE GREENAWAY | POUR | 1892 | PARIS:
LIBRAIRIE HACHETTE ET CIE, printed in black and white;
picture of young woman holding an overturned basket with
scattered flowers and cupids, printed in colors on gold background. *Spine:* light green cloth. *Back cover:* same as front cover.
All edges stained yellow. Turquoise endpapers.

"Gravé et imprimé par Edmund Evans, Racquet Court,
Londres," p. [24].

Presented by John S. Newberry.

44. Greenaway, Kate
ALMANACH | DE | KATE GREENAWAY | pour | 1893 |
PARIS: LIBRAIRIE HACHETTE ET CIE.

[36] p. 9.9 cm.

Cream-colored glazed pictorial boards. *Front cover:* AL-
MANACH | DE | KATE GREENAWAY | POUR 1893, printed in
black; picture of two small girls, one carrying a basket, the other
a nosegay, printed in colors. *Spine:* yellow cloth. *Back cover:* same
as front cover. All edges stained yellow. Blue endpapers.

"Gravé et imprimé par Edmund Evans, Racquet Court,
Londres," p. [36].

Presented by John S. Newberry.

45. Greenaway, Kate
ALMANACH | DE | KATE GREENAWAY | pour 1894 | PARIS:
LIBRAIRIE HACHETTE ET CIE.

[36] p. 9.8 cm.

Tan glazed pictorial boards. *Front cover:* ALMANACH | DE |
KATE GREENAWAY | pour 1894, printed in black; picture of
boy holding a bouquet of flowers and a girl holding her skirt full
of flowers, printed in colors. *Spine:* tan cloth. *Back cover:* same as
front cover. All edges stained green. Blue endpapers.

Cream-colored dust wrapper with "Almanach de Kate
Greenaway pour 1894" printed in brown on front cover.

"Londres: Gravé et imprimé par Edmund Evans, Racquet
Court," p. [36].

Contains the bookplate of F. Meunié.

Presented by John S. Newberry.

46. Greenaway, Kate
ALMANACH | DE | KATE GREENAWAY | POUR | 1895 |
PARIS: | LIBRAIRIE HACHETTE ET CIE.

[36] p. 10.0 cm.

Beige glazed pictorial boards. *Front cover:* ALMANACH | DE |
KATE GREENAWAY | pour 1895, printed in red and black;
picture of young boy holding a hoop and young girl in winter
attire, printed in colors. *Spine:* orange cloth. *Back cover:* same as
front cover. All edges stained yellow. Turquoise endpapers.

"Londres: Gravé et imprimé par Edmund Evans, Racquet
Court," p. [36].

Presented by John S. Newberry.

47. Greenaway, Kate
ALMANACK | FOR | 1883 | BY | KATE GREENAWAY | LON-
DON | GEORGE ROUTLEDGE AND SONS | BROADWAY,
LUDGATE HILL | NEW YORK: 9, LAFAYETTE PLACE.

[24] p. 9.9 cm.

"Engraved & Printed by Edmund Evans. The Pictures are
Copyright," p. [24].

a. Yellow glazed pictorial boards. *Front cover:* ONE SHILLING |
ALMANACK | FOR | 1883 | BY | KATE GREENAWAY, printed
in brown; same design as item 34. *Spine:* yellow cloth. *Back cover:*
same wording as front cover; same design as item 34. All edges
stained green. Turquoise endpapers.

Presented by John S. Newberry.

b. Yellow glazed pictorial boards. *Front cover:* same as item 47*a.*
Spine: yellow cloth. *Back cover:* same as item 47*a.* All edges

stained green. Turquoise endpapers.

Presentation inscription: "Mrs. Locker from Kate Greenaway Sept. 1882," p. [1].

Presented by John S. Newberry.

*c.** Yellow glazed pictorial boards. *Front cover:* same as item 47a. *Spine:* yellow cloth. *Back cover:* same as item 47a. All edges stained green. Turquoise endpapers.

Watercolor drawing measuring 3.8 cm. of small girl in white dress and bonnet holding a bouquet of red and pink roses, with the inscribed presentation "Ruth Anderson From Kate Greenaway 1891," p. [1].

Presented by John S. Newberry.

d. Brown roan, rounded corners. *Front cover:* Almanack | for 1883 | Kate Greenaway, stamped in gold; single-line border, stamped in dark brown. *Spine:* blank. *Back cover:* single-line border, stamped in dark brown. All edges gilt. Dark blue endpapers.

From the collection of Robert Partridge.

Presented by the Friends of the Detroit Public Library.

e. Yellow glazed pictorial boards. *Front cover:* ALMANACK | FOR | 1883 | BY | KATE GREENAWAY, printed in brown; same design as item 47a. *Spine:* yellow cloth. *Back cover:* same wording as front cover; same design as item 47a. All edges stained green. Turquoise endpapers.

No period at the end of the title page.

Presentation inscription: "Dorothy Locker from Kate Greenaway October 1882," p. [1].

Presented by John S. Newberry.

48. Greenaway, Kate
ALMANACK | FOR | 1884 | BY | KATE GREENAWAY | PRINTED BY EDMUND EVANS | LONDON: GEORGE ROUTLEDGE AND SONS | BROADWAY, LUDGATE HILL | NEW YORK: 9, LAFAYETTE PLACE | [Copyright]
[24] p.
"London Printed by Edmund Evans, Racquet Ct., Fleet St.," p. [6].

a. 13.3 cm.

White glazed pictorial wrappers. *Front cover:* ALMANACK FOR 1884 | BY | KATE GREENAWAY, printed in black; same design as item 35. *Spine:* blank. *Back cover:* same design as front

---

*Illustrated.

cover. Pages [1–2] and [23–24] used as pastedowns.
Presented by John S. Newberry.

b. 13.2 cm.

White imitation morocco wrappers. *Front cover:* KATE |
GREENAWAY'S | ALMANACK | 1884, stamped in gold; picture
of two girls carrying baskets of flowers, stamped in gold; four-
line border, blind-stamped. *Spine:* blank. *Back cover:* four-line
border, blind-stamped. All edges gilt. Pages [1–2] and [23–24]
used as pastedowns.
Presented by John S. Newberry.

c. 13.1 cm.

Light green imitation morocco wrappers. *Front cover:* same as
item 48*b*. *Spine:* blank. *Back cover:* same as item 48*b*. All edges
gilt. Pages [1–2] and [23–24] used as pastedowns.
Presentation inscription: "Dorothy J. C. Locker from Kate
Greenaway 1883," p. [3].
Presented by John S. Newberry.

*d.** 13.1 cm.

Light green imitation morocco wrappers. *Front cover:* same as
item 48*b*. *Spine:* blank. *Back cover:* same as item 48*b*. All edges
gilt. Pages [1–2] and [23–24] used as pastedowns.
Watercolor drawing measuring 3.3 cm. of young girl in red
dress and straw bonnet with black ribbons carrying a book
under her arm, with the inscribed presentation "Kenneth Anderson From Kate Greenaway 1891," p. [3].
Presented by John S. Newberry.

e. 13.2 cm.

White imitation morocco boards. *Front cover:* same as item 48*b*.
Spine: blank. *Back cover:* same as item 48*b*. All edges gilt. White
pastedowns.
Presentation inscription: "Mrs. Locker from Kate Greenaway
Dec. 1883," p. [1].
Presented by John S. Newberry.

49. Greenaway, Kate
    ALMANACK | FOR | 1885 | BY | KATE GREENAWAY | LON-
    DON | GEORGE ROUTLEDGE AND SONS | BROADWAY,
    LUDGATE HILL | NEW YORK: 9 LAFAYETTE PLACE
        [24] p. 10.0 cm.

*Illustrated.

"Engraved & Printed by Edmund Evans. The Pictures are Copyright," p. [24].

a. Cream-colored glazed pictorial boards. *Front cover:* AL-MANACK | 1885 | BY KATE GREENAWAY, printed in brown; same design as item 36. *Spine:* yellow cloth. *Back cover:* same design as item 36. All edges stained yellow. Blue endpapers.

Presented by John S. Newberry.

b. Cream-colored glazed pictorial boards. *Front cover:* same as item 49*a*. *Spine:* yellow cloth. *Back cover:* same as item 49*a*. All edges stained yellow. Dark gray endpapers.

Presentation inscription: "Dorothy Locker Lampson From Kate Greenaway 1892," p. [1].

Presented by John S. Newberry.

c. White imitation morocco boards. *Front cover:* ALMANACK | FOR | 1885 | BY | KATE GREENAWAY., stamped in gold; triple-line border, stamped in gold. *Spine:* blank. *Back cover:* triple-line border, blind-stamped. All edges gilt. Bright yellow endpapers.

Watercolor drawing measuring 2.8 cm. of a spray of white daffodils and leaves, with the inscribed presentation "Ruth Anderson From Kate Greenaway 1891," p. [1].

Presented by John S. Newberry.

50. Greenaway, Kate
ALMANACK | FOR | 1886 | By | KATE GREENAWAY | London: | GEORGE ROUTLEDGE & SONS | Broadway, Ludgate Hill. | New York: 9, Lafayette Place.
[24] p. 10.0 cm.
"The pictures are copyright. London: Printed by Edmund Evans, Racquet-Ct., Fleet-St.," p. [24].

a. Olive green glazed pictorial boards. *Front cover:* AL-MANACK 1886 | BY | KATE GREENAWAY, printed in brown; same design as item 37. *Spine:* orange cloth. *Back cover:* same design as item 37. All edges stained blue. Bright yellow endpapers.

Presentation inscription: "Dorothy Locker-Lampson From Kate Greenaway 1886," p. [1].

Presented by John S. Newberry.

b. Olive green glazed pictorial boards. *Front cover:* same as item 50*a*. *Spine:* orange cloth. *Back cover:* same as item 50*a*. All edges stained blue. Bright yellow endpapers.

White dust wrapper with "Kate Greenaway's Almanack for 1886" on front cover.

Presentation inscription: "Frederick Locker from Kate Greenaway 1886," p. [1].
Presented by John S. Newberry.

c. White imitation morocco boards. *Front cover:* ALMANACK | FOR | 1886 | BY | KATE GREENAWAY, stamped in gold; picture of young girl holding her skirt full of flowers, stamped in gold; ornamental border, stamped in blue. *Spine:* blank. *Back cover:* ornamental border, stamped in blue. All edges gilt. Bright yellow endpapers.
Presented by John S. Newberry.

d. White imitation morocco boards. *Front cover:* same as item 50*c*. *Spine:* blank. *Back cover:* same as item 50*c*. All edges gilt. Bright yellow endpapers.
Presentation inscription: "Dorothy Locker Lampson From Kate Greenaway 1892," p. [1].
Presented by John S. Newberry.

51. Greenaway, Kate
ALMANACK | FOR 1887 | BY | KATE GREENAWAY | GEORGE ROUTLEDGE & SONS | The Pictures are Copyright.
[24] p. Oblong. 7.1 x 10.2 cm.
a. Cream-colored glazed pictorial boards. *Front cover:* ALMANACK FOR 1887 | BY | KATE GREENAWAY, printed in black; same design as item 38. *Spine:* yellow cloth. *Back cover:* same as front cover. All edges stained green. Light blue endpapers.
Presented by John S. Newberry.

b. Cream-colored glazed pictorial boards. *Front cover:* same as item 51*a*. *Spine:* yellow cloth. *Back cover:* same as front cover. All edges stained green. Turquoise endpapers.
Presentation inscription: "F Locker Lampson Esq. From Kate Greenaway. 1886," p. [1].
Presented by John S. Newberry.

c. Blue cloth. *Front cover:* same as item 51*a*, stamped in gold. *Spine:* blank. *Back cover:* blank. All edges gilt. Bright yellow endpapers.
Presentation inscription: "Dorothy Locker-Lampson From Kate Greenaway 1892," p. [1].
Presented by John S. Newberry.

d. Salmon cloth. *Front cover:* same as item 51*a*, stamped in gold. *Spine:* blank. *Back cover:* blank. All edges gilt. Bright yellow endpapers.

Cream-colored glazed pictorial cover (same as item 51*a*) pasted on inside front cover.

From the collection of Robert Partridge.

Presented by the Friends of the Detroit Public Library.

52. Greenaway, Kate
KATE GREENAWAY'S | ALMANACK | FOR | 1888 | GEORGE ROUTLEDGE & SONS
[24] p. 9.9. cm.
a. Yellow glazed pictorial boards. *Front cover:* ALMANACK | For | 1888 | Kate Greenaway, printed in brown; same design as item 39. *Spine:* blue cloth. *Back cover:* same as front cover. All edges stained blue. Dark blue endpapers.
Presentation inscription: "Dorothy Locker Lampson from Kate Greenaway 1887," p. [1].
Presented by John S. Newberry.

b. Yellow glazed pictorial boards. *Front cover:* same as item 52a. Spine: blue cloth. *Back cover:* same as front cover. All edges stained blue. Dark blue endpapers.
Watercolor drawing measuring 3.5 cm. of a young woman in a long red dress holding a baby, with a potted shrub in the background, with the inscribed presentation "Ruth Anderson From Kate Greenaway 1891," p. [1].
Presented by John S. Newberry.

c. Light brown cloth. *Front cover:* ALMANACK | FOR | 1888 | BY | KATE GREENAWAY, stamped in gold; picture of back view of two girls, stamped in gold; decorative border, stamped in blue. *Spine:* blank. *Back cover:* decorative border, stamped in blue. All edges gilt. Bright yellow endpapers.
Presented by John S. Newberry.

d. Cream-colored cloth. *Front cover:* same as item 52c. *Spine:* blank. *Back cover:* same as item 52c. All edges gilt. Bright yellow endpapers.
Presentation inscription: "Dorothy Locker Lampson From Kate Greenaway 1892," p. [1].
Presented by John S. Newberry.

53. Greenaway, Kate
ALMANACK | FOR | 1889 | BY | KATE GREENAWAY | Printed by Edmund Evans | GEORGE ROUTLEDGE AND

SONS | LONDON, GLASGOW, AND NEW YORK

[24] p. 9.8 cm.

a. Black glazed pictorial boards. *Front cover:* ALMANACK | FOR |1889 | BY | KATE GREENAWAY | LONDON: GEORGE ROUTLEDGE & SONS | BROADWAY, LUDGATE HILL | GLAS- GOW AND NEW YORK, printed in white; same design as item 40. *Spine:* black cloth. *Back cover:* same design as item 40. All edges stained yellow. Bright yellow endpapers.

Presentation inscription: "Dorothy Locker Lampson From Kate Greenaway 1892," p. [1].

Presented by John S. Newberry.

b. Tan cloth. *Front cover:* ALMANACK | FOR | 1889 | BY | KATE GREENAWAY., stamped in gold; picture of seated girl reading a book, stamped in gold; decorative border, stamped in blue. *Spine:* blank. *Back cover:* decorative border, stamped in blue. All edges gilt. Blue endpapers.

Presented by John S. Newberry.

c. Tan cloth. *Front cover:* same as item 53*b*. *Spine:* blank. *Back cover:* same as item 53*b*. All edges gilt. Blue endpapers.

Presentation inscription: "The Hon'ble. Gerald Ponsonby From Kate Greenaway Jan 1889," p. [1].

Presented by John S. Newberry.

d. Tan cloth. *Front cover:* same as item 53*b*. *Spine:* blank. *Back cover:* same as item 53*b*. All edges gilt. Blue endpapers.

Inscribed: "Kate Greenaway Dec. 1888," p. [1].

Presented by John S. Newberry.

54. Greenaway, Kate

ALMANACK | FOR | 1890 | BY | KATE GREENAWAY | En- graved & Printed by E. Evans | GEORGE ROUTLEDGE & SONS

[24] p. 9.9 cm.

a. Black glazed pictorial boards. *Front cover:* ALMANACK | FOR | 1890 | BY KATE GREENAWAY, printed in white; same design as item 41. *Spine:* black cloth. *Back cover:* same design as item 41. All edges stained yellow. Bright yellow endpapers.

Presented by John S. Newberry.

b. Black glazed pictorial boards. *Front cover:* same as item 54*a*. *Spine:* black cloth. *Back cover:* same as item 54*a*. All edges stained yellow. Bright yellow endpapers.

Presentation inscription: "Miss Fripp from Kate Greenaway

Dec 1889," p. [1].

Presented by John S. Newberry.

c. Light green cloth. *Front cover:* ALMANACK | FOR | 1890 | BY | KATE GREENAWAY, stamped in gold; picture of young girl holding flowers in her skirt, stamped in gold; vine and rule border, stamped in blue. *Spine:* blank. *Back cover:* vine and rule border, stamped in blue. All edges gilt. Blue endpapers.

Presentation inscription: "Dorothy Locker Lampson From Kate Greenaway 1892," p. [1].

Presented by John S. Newberry.

55. Greenaway, Kate
ALMANACK | FOR | 1891 | GEORGE ROUTLEDGE & SONS, LIMITED

[24] p. 10.0 cm.

White glazed pictorial boards. *Front cover:* KATE | GREEN-AWAY'S | ALMANACK | FOR | 1891 | GEORGE ROUTLEDGE & SONS | LIMITED, printed in blue; same design as item 42. *Spine:* yellow cloth. *Back cover:* same wording as front cover; same design as item 42. All edges stained yellow. Turquoise endpapers.

"London, Engraved & Printed at Racquet Court, by Edmund Evans," p. [24].

Presented by John S. Newberry.

56. Greenaway, Kate
KATE | GREENAWAY'S | ALMANACK | FOR | 1891 | GEORGE ROUTLEDGE & SONS, LIMITED

[24] p. 10.2 cm.

"London Engraved & Printed at Racquet Court, by Edmund Evans," p. [24].

a. Cream-colored imitation morocco boards. *Front cover:* KATE | GREENAWAY'S | ALMANACK | FOR | 1891., stamped in gold; same picture as item 42, stamped in gold; same border as item 42, stamped in brown. *Spine:* blank. *Back cover:* wide leafy border, stamped in brown. All edges gilt. Blue endpapers.

Presentation inscription: "Dorothy Locker Lampson From Kate Greenaway 1892," p. [1].

Presented by John S. Newberry.

b. Cream-colored imitation morocco boards. *Front cover:* same as item 56*a*. *Spine:* blank. *Back cover:* same as item 56*a*. All edges gilt. Blue endpapers.

Watercolor drawing measuring 1.6 cm. showing ivy vine

with the inscribed presentation "Ruth Anderson From Kate Greenaway Dec 1890," p. [1].

Presented by John S. Newberry.

57. Greenaway, Kate
KATE GREENAWAY'S | ALMANACK | FOR | 1892 | GEORGE ROUTLEDGE & SONS, Limited.

[24] p. 10.0 cm.

"London Engraved & Printed at Racquet Court by Edmund Evans," p. [24].

a. Cream-colored glazed pictorial boards. *Front cover:* KATE GREENAWAY'S | ALMANACK | FOR | 1892, printed in black and white; same design as item 43. *Spine:* light green cloth. *Back cover:* same as front cover. All edges stained yellow. Blue end-papers.

Presented by John S. Newberry.

b. Cream-colored glazed pictorial boards. *Front cover:* same as item 57a. *Spine:* bright blue cloth. *Back cover:* same as front cover. All edges stained yellow. Dark green endpapers.

White dust wrapper with "Kate Greenaway's Almanack for 1892" and the outline of a postage stamp printed in brown on front cover.

Presentation inscription: "Dorothy Locker-Lampson From Kate Greenaway 1892," p. [1].

Presented by John S. Newberry.

c. Cream-colored imitation morocco boards. *Front cover:* KATE | GREENAWAY'S | ALMANACK | FOR | 1892., stamped in gold; picture of boy and girl dancing, stamped in gold; decorative border, stamped in green. *Spine:* blank. *Back cover:* decorative border, stamped in green. All edges gilt. Dark blue endpapers.

Watercolor drawing measuring 3.8 cm. of baby in white plumed bonnet and fur-trimmed blue coat with the inscribed presentation "Dorothy Locker Lampson From Kate Greenaway 1891," p. [1].

Presented by John S. Newberry.

58. Greenaway, Kate
KATE GREENAWAY'S | ALMANACK | for 1893 | GEORGE ROUTLEDGE & SONS, LIMITED

[36] p. 10.0 cm.

"London Engraved & Printed at Racquet Court, by Edmund Evans," p. [36].

a. Cream-colored glazed pictorial boards. *Front cover:* KATE GREENAWAY'S | ALMANACK | FOR 1893., printed in brown; same design as item 44. *Spine:* yellow cloth. *Back cover:* same as front cover. All edges stained green. Blue endpapers.

Presented by John S. Newberry.

b. Cream-colored glazed pictorial boards. *Front cover:* same as item 58*a. Spine:* yellow cloth. *Back cover:* same as front cover. All edges stained green. Blue endpapers.

Presentation inscription: "Dorothy Locker Lampson From Kate Greenaway 1892," p. [1].

Presented by John S. Newberry.

c. Olive green silk. *Front cover:* Kate Greenaway's | AL-MANACK | FOR | 1893, stamped in gold; double-line border, stamped in gold. *Spine:* blank. *Back cover:* double-line border, blind-stamped. All edges stained pink. Turquoise endpapers.

Watercolor drawing measuring 3 cm. of small girl in black bonnet and fur-trimmed red coat with the inscribed presentation "Ruth Anderson From Kate Greenaway 1892," p. [1].

Presented by John S. Newberry.

59. Greenaway, Kate
KATE GREENAWAY'S | ALMANACK | for 1894 | GEORGE ROUTLEDGE & SONS, LIMITED
[36] p. 10.0 cm.
"London Engraved & Printed at Racquet Court, by Edmund Evans," p. [36].

a. Tan glazed pictorial boards. *Front cover:* KATE GREEN-AWAY'S | ALMANACK | for 1894, printed in black; same design as item 45. *Spine:* tan cloth. *Back cover:* same as front cover. All edges stained green. Dark blue endpapers.

Presented by John S. Newberry.

b. Tan glazed pictorial boards. *Front cover:* same as item 59*a. Spine:* tan cloth. *Back cover:* same as front cover. All edges stained green. Blue endpapers.

Presentation inscription: "Dorothy Locker-Lampson From Kate Greenaway Dec. 1893," p. [1].

Presented by John S. Newberry.

c. Tan glazed pictorial boards. *Front cover:* same as item 59*a. Spine:* tan cloth. *Back cover:* same as front cover. All edges stained green. Turquoise endpapers.

Presentation inscription: "Ruth Anderson From Kate

Greenaway Dec 1893," p. [1].
Presented by John S. Newberry.

d. Cream-colored imitation morocco. *Front cover:* AL-MANACK | FOR | 1894 | BY | KATE GREENAWAY, stamped in gold; picture of girl holding her skirt full of flowers, stamped in gold; decorative border, stamped in blue. *Spine:* blank. *Back cover:* decorative border, stamped in blue. All edges gilt. Dark blue endpapers.

From the collection of Robert Partridge.

Presented by the Friends of the Detroit Public Library.

60. Greenaway, Kate
KATE GREENAWAY'S | ALMANACK | FOR | 1895 | GEORGE ROUTLEDGE & SONS, | LIMITED.
[36] p. 10.0 cm.
"London Engraved & Printed at Racquet Court, by Edmund Evans," p. [36].

a. Cream-colored glazed pictorial boards. *Front cover:* KATE GREENAWAY'S |ALMANACK | for 1895, printed in brown and orange; same design as item 46. *Spine:* orange cloth. *Back cover:* same as front cover. All edges stained yellow. Turquoise endpapers.

Presented by John S. Newberry.

b. Cream-colored glazed pictorial boards. *Front cover:* same as item 60*a*. *Spine:* orange cloth. *Back cover:* same as front cover. All edges stained yellow. Turquoise endpapers.

Presentation inscription: "Dorothy From Kate Greenaway 1894," p. [1].

Presented by John S. Newberry.

c. Cream-colored glazed pictorial boards. *Front cover:* same as item 60*a*. *Spine:* orange cloth. *Back cover:* same as front cover. All edges stained yellow. Turquoise endpapers.

Pencil and watercolor drawing measuring 2.2 cm. of a girl's head with the inscribed presentation "Ruth Anderson From Kate Greenaway 1894," p. [1].

Presented by John S. Newberry.

61. Greenaway, Kate
KATE | GREENAWAY'S | ALMANACK | & DIARY for | 1897. | J. M. DENT & CO: | 67 ST. JAMES'S ST: LONDON
[72] p. 10.3 cm.
"London Engraved & Printed at Racquet Court, by Edmund

Evans," p. [72].

    a. Mustard-colored imitation morocco. *Front cover:* KATE GREENAWAY'S | ALMANACK | & DIARY for 1897, stamped in gold; picture of woman carrying sticks, stamped in gold. *Spine:* blank. *Back cover:* blank. Top edge gilt. White endpapers.

    Presented by John S. Newberry.

    b. Mustard-colored imitation morocco. *Front cover:* same as item 61*a*. *Spine:* blank. *Back cover:* blank. Top edge gilt. White endpapers.

    Presentation inscription: "Dorothy Locker-Lampson From Kate Greenaway 1896," p. [1].

    Presented by John S. Newberry.

    c. Mustard-colored imitation morocco. *Front cover:* same as item 61*a*. *Spine:* blank. *Back cover:* blank. Top edge gilt. White endpapers.

    Watercolor drawing measuring 3.6 cm. of small girl in violet bonnet and fur-trimmed maroon coat with the inscribed presentation "Ruth Anderson From Kate Greenaway 1896," p. [1].

    Presented by John S. Newberry.

62.   Greenaway, Kate
    ALMANACK | FOR | 1924 | BY | KATE GREENAWAY | LONDON | FREDERICK WARNE & CO. LTD. | AND NEW YORK | [All rights reserved]
    [24] p. 9.7 cm.
    White glazed pictorial boards. *Front cover:* ALMANACK FOR 1924 | BY KATE GREENAWAY, printed in yellow; picture of young girl in bonnet, cape, and long dress, printed in colors; triple-line border, printed in yellow. *Spine:* yellow cloth. *Back cover:* same as front cover. All edges stained blue. Cream-colored endpapers.
    "The Coloured Illustrations are the actual first printing of the 1883 Almanack. The Text for the Year 1924 is now inserted," glassine wrapper.
    "Engraved & Printed by Edmund Evans," p. [24].
    Presented by the Friends of the Detroit Public Library.

63.   Greenaway, Kate
    ALMANACK | FOR 1925 | BY | KATE GREENAWAY | FREDERICK WARNE & CO., LTD. | (All rights reserved)
    [24] p. Oblong. 7.4 x 10.5 cm.
    Cream-colored glazed pictorial boards. *Front cover:* ALMANACK FOR 1925 | BY | KATE GREENAWAY, stamped in

51

black; same design as item 38. *Spine:* yellow cloth. *Back cover:* same as front cover. All edges stained yellow. White endpapers.

"Printed in Great Britain," p. [4].

The colored illustrations are those used in the 1887 *Almanack*. The text has been revised for the year 1925.

Presented by the Friends of the Detroit Public Library.

64. Greenaway, Kate

ALMANACK | FOR | 1926 | BY | KATE GREENAWAY | Engraved & Printed by E. Evans | FREDERICK WARNE & Co LTD

[24] p. 9.9 cm.

Black glazed pictorial boards. *Front cover:* ALMANACK | FOR | 1926 | BY KATE GREENAWAY, printed in white; same design as item 41. *Spine:* black cloth. *Back cover:* same design as item 41. All edges stained yellow. Yellow endpapers.

"Printed in Great Britain," p. [4].

The colored illustrations are those used in the 1890 *Almanack*. The text has been revised for the year 1926.

From the collection of Robert Partridge.

Presented by the Friends of the Detroit Public Library.

65. Greenaway, Kate

KATE | GREENAWAY'S | ALMANACK | FOR | 1927 | FREDERICK WARNE & CO., LTD. | All rights reserved.

[24] p. 10.3 cm.

Cream-colored glazed pictorial boards. *Front cover:* KATE | GREENAWAY'S | ALMANACK | FOR | 1927., printed in black; same design as item 42. *Spine:* yellow cloth. *Back cover:* same wording as front cover; same design as item 42. All edges stained yellow. Bright yellow endpapers.

"The coloured illustrations are the actual first printing of the 1891 *Almanack*. The text for the year 1927 is now inserted," glassine wrapper.

"London Engraved & Printed at Racquet Court by Edmund Evans," p. [24].

Presented by the Friends of the Detroit Public Library.

66. Greenaway, Kate

KATE GREENAWAY'S | ALMANACK | for 1928. | FREDERICK WARNE & CO. LTD. | All rights reserved

[36] p. 10.4 cm.

Tan glazed pictorial boards. *Front cover:* KATE GREENAWAY'S | ALMANACK | for 1928, printed in black; same design as item 45. *Spine:* light brown cloth. *Back cover:* same wording as front cover; same design as item 45. All edges stained light green. White endpapers.

"The coloured illustrations are the actual first printing of the 1894 *Almanack*. The text for the year 1928 is now inserted," glassine wrapper.

"Printed in Great Britain," p. [6].

From the collection of Robert Partridge.

Presented by the Friends of the Detroit Public Library.

67. Greenaway, Kate

KATE | GREENAWAY'S | ALMANACK | & DIARY for | 1929. | FREDERICK WARNE & CO LTD | LONDON & NEW YORK

[72] p. 10.1 cm.

Green imitation morocco. *Front cover:* KATE GREENAWAY'S | ALMANACK | & DIARY for 1929., stamped in gold; same design as item 61a. *Spine:* blank. *Back cover:* blank. Top edge gilt. White endpapers.

"Engraved and printed by Edmund Evans Ltd., Rose Place, Globe Road, London, E.1," p. [72].

Presentation inscription: "With all good wishes for Christmas and the New Year from John Greenaway," recto front flyleaf.

The colored illustrations are those used in the 1897 *Almanack*. The text has been revised for the year 1929.

From the collection of Robert Partridge.

Presented by the Friends of the Detroit Public Library.

68. Greenaway, Kate

KATE GREENAWAY'S | ALPHABET | LONDON | GEORGE ROUTLEDGE & SONS | BROADWAY LUDGATE HILL. | NEW YORK: 9, LAFAYETTE PLACE.

[32] p.

a. 6.7 cm.

Yellow glazed wrappers. *Front cover:* KATE GREENAWAY'S | ALPHABET, printed in brown; picture of seated woman reading to a child, printed in colors. *Spine:* printed in green. *Back cover:* same as front cover.

Presented by John S. Newberry.

b. 7.0 cm.

Yellow glazed pictorial boards. *Front cover:* same as item 68a. *Spine:* printed in green. *Back cover:* same as front cover. White endpapers.

Presented by the Friends of the Detroit Public Library.

c. 6.9 cm.

White pictorial boards. *Front cover:* same as item 68a. *Spine:*

blank. *Back cover:* blank. All edges stained yellow. White end-papers.

Presented by the Friends of the Detroit Public Library.

69. Greenaway, Kate

ALPHABET | PAR | KATE GREENAWAY | PARIS | LIB-RAIRIE HACHETTE ET CIE. | 79, BOULEVARD SAINT-GERMAIN, 79

[32] p. 6.7 cm.

Yellow glazed pictorial wrappers. *Front cover:* picture of seated woman reading to a child, printed in colors. *Spine:* printed in green. *Back cover:* same as front cover.

Presented by the Friends of the Detroit Public Library.

70.* Greenaway, Kate

AM FENSTER. | IN BILDERN UND VERSEN | VON | KATE GREENAWAY. | DER DEUTSCHE TEXT | VON | KÄTHE FREILIGRATH-KROEKER. | MÜNCHEN: | THEODOR STROEFER'S | KUNSTVERLAG. | (GESETZLICH GE-SCHÜTZT)

[6] 7–64 [65–66] p. 23.2 cm.

Dark green glazed pictorial boards. *Front cover:* AM FENSTER | in | BILDERN UND VERSEN | von | Kate Greenaway, printed in red and black; a procession of children surrounding title, printed in white; single-line border, printed in black. *Spine:* blue cloth. *Back cover:* same as front cover. All edges stained orange. Blue endpapers.

"In Farbigem Holzschnitt Ausgeführt und Gedruckt von Edmund Evans.," p. [65].

Contains the bookplate of E. H. Mills.

Tipped in is a receipt made out to Edmund Evans, on April 20, 1880, for £166 13/4, the royalty on ten thousand copies of *Under the Window* (three thousand in German and seven thousand in English), signed by K.G.

Presented by John S. Newberry.

71. Greenaway, Kate

KATE GREENAWAY'S | BIRTHDAY BOOK | for Children | WITH 382 ILLUSTRATIONS, | DRAWN BY KATE GREEN-AWAY, | PRINTED BY EDMUND EVANS. | VERSES BY MRS. SALE BARKER. | LONDON: | GEORGE ROUTLEDGE AND SONS, | BROADWAY, LUDGATE HILL. | NEW YORK: 416 BROOME STREET. | [ALL RIGHTS RESERVED.]

---

*Illustrated.

[vi] [4] 5–126 [127–32] p. (i.e., 272 p.)

"London. Engraved & printed at Racquet Court by Edmund Evans," p. [130].

a. 9.1 cm.

Beige cloth. *Front cover:* KATE GREENAWAY'S | BIRTHDAY | BOOK | for | Children, stamped in brown; pictures representing the four seasons, one in each corner, stamped in colors. *Spine:* five sets of four lines, stamped in blue. *Back cover:* same as front cover. All edges stained yellow. Blue endpapers.

Inscription dated "1880," p. [ii].

Presented by John S. Newberry.

b. 9.1 cm.

Olive green cloth, beveled edges. *Front cover:* Kate Green-away's | BIRTHDAY BOOK | for | CHILDREN, stamped in gold; round picture of young boy and girl holding hands, printed in colors on glazed paper, pasted in lower left-hand corner; flow-ers and branches, stamped in black and gold. *Spine:* Birthday | Book | for | Children | Kate | Greenaway, stamped in gold; leaves, stamped in black. *Back cover:* dragonfly and flowers, stamped in gold and black. All edges gilt. Blue endpapers.

From the collection of Robert Partridge.

Presented by the Friends of the Detroit Public Library.

c. 9.4 cm.

Gold velvet, with metal clasp. *Front cover:* blank. *Spine:* blank. *Back cover:* blank. All edges gilt. Gray and white floral endpapers.

Presented by the Friends of the Detroit Public Library.

d. 9.1 cm.

Cream-colored glazed pictorial boards. *Front cover:* picture of sailor boy, signed "K.G.," printed in colors. *Spine:* blue cloth. *Back cover:* blank. All edges stained yellow. Brown and white decorative endpapers.

Copy imperfect, lacking pp. [i–ii].

Presented by the Friends of the Detroit Public Library.

72.   Greenaway, Kate

KATE GREENAWAY'S | BIRTHDAY BOOK | for Children | WITH 382 ILLUSTRATIONS, | DRAWN BY KATE GREEN-AWAY, | PRINTED BY EDMUND EVANS. | VERSES BY MRS. SALE BARKER. | LONDON | FREDERICK WARNE AND CO. | AND NEW YORK | [ALL RIGHTS RESERVED.

[vi] [4] 5–126 [127–132] p. (i.e., 272 p.) 9.1 cm.

Beige cloth. *Front cover:* same as item 71*a. Spine:* same as item

71a. *Back cover:* same as item 71a. Dark blue endpapers.

"London. Engraved & Printed at the Racquet Court Press by Edmund Evans," p. [130].

Inscription dated "Xmas 1901," p. [ii].

From the collection of Robert Partridge.

Presented by the Friends of the Detroit Public Library.

73. Greenaway, Kate

KATE GREENAWAY'S | BOOK OF GAMES | With Twenty-four Full-page Plates | ENGRAVED AND PRINTED IN COL-OURS BY EDMUND EVANS | LONDON | GEORGE ROUT-LEDGE & SONS | BROADWAY, LUDGATE HILL | GLAS-GOW, MANCHESTER, AND NEW YORK

[10] 11–63 [64] p. 23.1 cm.

"Engraved and Printed in Colours by Edmund Evans Racquet Court, Fleet Street, London, E.C," p. [64].

a. Green glazed pictorial boards. *Front cover:* KATE | GREENAWAY'S | BOOK OF | GAMES | GEORGE ROUT-LEDGE & SONS, printed in green and black; picture of children on a seesaw, printed in colors. *Spine:* blue cloth. *Back cover:* same as front cover. All edges stained yellow. Bright yellow endpapers.

Contains the bookplate of Charles Plumptre Johnson.

From the collection of Robert Partridge.

Presented by the Friends of the Detroit Public Library.

b. Gold cloth. *Front cover:* KATE | GREENAWAY'S | BOOK OF GAMES | WITH | COLOURED | ILLUSTRATIONS, stamped in gold and black; picture of two boys playing with a top and picture of girls playing blind man's buff, stamped in colors; top border design of flowers, stamped in black and yellow. *Spine:* blank. *Back cover:* blank. All edges stained yellow. Bright yellow endpapers.

Presented by John S. Newberry.

c. Light green cloth. *Front cover:* same as item 73b. *Spine:* blank. *Back cover:* blank. All edges stained yellow. Bright yellow endpapers.

Contains the bookplate of Charles Plumptre Johnson.

From the collection of Robert Partridge.

Presented by the Friends of the Detroit Public Library.

d. Blue cloth. *Front cover:* same as item 73b. *Spine:* blank. *Back cover:* blank. All edges stained yellow. Bright yellow endpapers.

Presented by the Friends of the Detroit Public Library.

74. Greenaway, Kate
   KATE GREENAWAY'S | BOOK OF GAMES | With Twenty-four Colour Plates | FREDERICK WARNE & CO., LTD. | LONDON & NEW YORK

   [10] 11–63 [64] p. 22.3 cm.

   Green glazed pictorial boards. *Front cover:* KATE | GREENAWAY'S | BOOK OF | GAMES | Frederick Warne & Co., Ltd., printed in green and black; picture of children on a seesaw, printed in colors. *Spine:* green cloth; KATE GREENAWAY'S BOOK OF GAMES, stamped in dark green. *Back cover:* same as front cover. All edges stained green. White endpapers.

   "Printed in Great Britain," p. [6].

   From the collection of Robert Partridge.

   Presented by the Friends of the Detroit Public Library.

75. Greenaway, Kate
   KATE GREENAWAY'S | Börnebilleder | 2det Opl: | med Vers af | CHRISTOPHER BOECK. | GYLDENDALSKE BOGHANDEL | NORDISK FORLAG | NORDISK | REPRODUKTIONS-ANSTALT | KIAREBODERNE 3.

   [ii] [1] 2–28 [29] l. 22.9 cm.

   Green glazed pictorial boards. *Front cover:* wording same as title page, printed in black; picture of six small children standing in a row holding hands and two children seated, printed in colors. *Spine:* black cloth. *Back cover:* circle in center containing picture of young girl in long dress, bonnet, and fan in hand, printed in colors. White pastedowns.

   Printing only on recto of each leaf; verso blank.

   Scandinavian edition of selections from *Under the Window.*

   Presented by the Friends of the Detroit Public Library.

76. Greenaway, Kate
   HISTOIRE | D'UNE | Tourte aux Pommes | ILLUSTRATIONS DE KATE GREENAWAY | INTERPRÉTATION DE J. GIRARDIN | PARIS | LIBRAIRIE HACHETTE ET CIE | 79, BOULEVARD SAINT-GERMAIN, 79 | 1886

   [44] p. Oblong. 21.3 x 26.0 cm.

   Light green glazed pictorial boards. *Front cover:* HISTOIRE D'UNE Tourte | aux | Pommes | PAR | KATE GREENAWAY, printed in black and red; same design as item 33*a*. *Spine:* red cloth. *Back cover:* same as front cover. All edges stained red. Dark blue endpapers.

   "Gravé et Imprimé par Edmond Evans, Racquet Court, Fleet Street, Londres," p. [4].

French edition of *A Apple Pie*.
Presented by the Friends of the Detroit Public Library.

77. Greenaway, Kate
JEUX | ET | PASSE-TEMPS | Avec 24 Planches en Couleurs | D'APRÈS | KATE GREENAWAY | PARIS | LIBRAIRIE HACHETTE ET CIE | 79, BOULEVARD SAINT-GERMAIN, 79 | 1890
[10] 11–63 [64] p. 23.3 cm.
Light blue glazed pictorial boards. *Front cover:* JEUX | ET | PASSE-TEMPS | Avec 24 Planches en Couleurs | D'APRÈS | KATE GREENAWAY | PARIS | LIBRAIRIE HACHETTE ET CIE | 79, BOULEVARD SAINT-GERMAIN, 79, printed in black; picture of children on a seesaw, printed in colors. *Spine:* blue cloth. *Back cover:* same as front cover. All edges stained yellow. Bright yellow endpapers.
"Gravé et Imprimé par Edmond Evans, Racquet Ct., Fleet St., Londres," p. [2].
"Gravé et Imprimé par Edmond Evans, Racquet Court, Fleet Street, Londres," p. [64].
French edition of *Book of Games*.
Presented by the Friends of the Detroit Public Library.

78. Greenaway, Kate
Le | Langage des Fleurs | ILLUSTRATIONS DE | KATE GREENAWAY | PARIS | LIBRAIRIE HACHETTE ET CIE., | 79, BOULEVARD ST. GERMAIN, 79. | [Droits de reproduction réservés.]
[6] 7–79 [80] p. 14.6 cm.
Green glazed pictorial boards. *Front cover:* Le Langage | des Fleurs | ILLUSTRATIONS | DE | KATE GREENAWAY, printed in black; picture of two young women, one holding a basket of flowers, the other holding her skirt full of flowers, leaning on a fence, with bottom border of roses, printed in colors on a cream-colored background. *Spine:* green cloth. *Back cover:* same as front cover. All edges stained yellow. Bright yellow endpapers.
Presented by John S. Newberry.

79. Greenaway, Kate
Language of Flowers | ILLUSTRATED BY | KATE GREENAWAY | PRINTED IN COLOURS BY | EDMUND EVANS | London: George Routledge and Sons
[6] 7–80 p.

a. 14.7 cm.

Green glazed pictorial boards. *Front cover:* Language | of Flowers | ILLUSTRATED | BY | KATE GREENAWAY, printed in brown; same design as item 78, printed in colors on a cream-colored background. *Spine:* green cloth. *Back cover:* same as front cover. All edges stained yellow. Bright yellow endpapers.

Contains the bookplate of E. H. M.

Presented by John S. Newberry.

b. 14.7 cm.

Green glazed pictorial boards. *Front cover:* same as item 79*a*. *Spine:* green cloth. *Back cover:* same as item 79*a*. All edges stained yellow. Bright yellow endpapers.

Pen-and-ink drawing measuring 2.2 cm. of two flowers with the inscribed presentation "Stuart M. Samuel From Kate Greenaway 1899," p. [1].

Contains the bookplate of E. H. Mills.

Presented by John S. Newberry.

c. 14.7 cm.

Green glazed pictorial boards. *Front cover:* The | Language | of Flowers | illustrated by | Kate Greenaway, printed in black; same design as item 79*a*, printed in colors on a dark red background. *Spine:* green cloth. *Back cover:* same as front cover. All edges stained yellow. Cream-colored endpapers.

Contains the bookplate of E. H. M.

Presented by John S. Newberry.

d. 14.7 cm.

Imitation white morocco boards. *Front cover:* KATE GREENAWAY'S | LANGUAGE | OF | FLOWERS, stamped in gold; flower and triple-line border, stamped in gold. *Spine:* blank. *Back cover:* triple-line border, blind-stamped. All edges gilt. Light green endpapers.

Contains the bookplate of E. H. M.

Presented by John S. Newberry.

e. 14.7 cm.

Imitation white morocco boards. *Front cover:* same as item 79*d*. *Spine:* blank. *Back cover:* same as item 79*d*. All edges gilt. Light green endpapers.

Presented by John S. Newberry.

f. 14.6 cm.

Imitation tan morocco boards. *Front cover:* same as item 79*d*.

Spine: blank. *Back cover:* same as item 79d. All edges gilt. Olive green endpapers.

Contains the bookplate of E. H. M.

Presented by John S. Newberry.

g. 14.6 cm.

Brown roan, rounded corners. *Front cover:* Language of Flowers, stamped in gold. *Spine:* blank. *Back cover:* blank. All edges gilt. Black endpapers.

From the collection of Robert Partridge.

Presented by the Friends of the Detroit Public Library.

80. Greenaway, Kate

LA LANTERNE MAGIQUE | PAR J. LEVOISIN. | AVEC LES DESSINS | DE | KATE GREENAWAY | PARIS | LIBRAIRIE HACHETTE ET CIE | 79, BOULEVARD SAINT-GERMAIN, 79

[6] 7–64 [65–66] p. 23.3 cm.

Green glazed pictorial boards. *Front cover:* LA | LANTERNE | MAGIQUE | par | J. Levoisin | avec les dessins | de Kate Greenaway, printed in red and black; a circular procession of children, printed in white on an olive green background. *Spine:* blue cloth. *Back cover:* same as front cover. All edges stained red. Blue endpapers.

"Gravé et Imprimé par Edmund Evans," p. [65].

French translation of *Under the Window.*

Presented by the Friends of the Detroit Public Library.

81. Greenaway, Kate

THE LITTLE FOLKS | PAINTING BOOK | BY | KATE | GREENAWAY | McLOUGHLIN BROS, N.Y.

[34] p. 23.8 cm.

Pictorial boards. *Front cover:* THE LITTLE FOLKS | PAINTING BOOK | BY | KATE | GREENAWAY | McLOUGHLIN BROS, N.Y, printed in dark red and blue; picture enclosed in a circle of young boy painting and several children watching, printed in colors. *Spine:* red cloth. *Back cover:* yellow board; advertisement for "Pantomime Toy Books."

Title taken from cover.

"The Little Folks' Painting Book... A Few Practical Directions... Instructions for Mixing the Colors...," verso front cover.

Advertisement for McLoughlin Bros. publications, recto back cover.

Printing on one side of sheet only. Illustrations on p. [1] printed in colors, the rest in brown and white.

82. Greenaway, Kate

"Little Men & Women" | from the pages of | KATE GREENAWAY

[4] p. 16.0 cm., sixteen individually mounted pictures. 23.2 cm.

Portfolio. Beige boards. *Front cover:* LITTLE MEN AND WOMEN | FROM THE PAGES OF | KATE GREENAWAY | F.A.R. GALLERY, printed in black; title surrounded by garland of roses, printed in colors. *Spine:* dark green cloth. *Back cover:* blank.

Four-page introduction signed Herman J. Wechsler.

"Published by F. A. R. Gallery 1946, all contents Copyright," p. [4].

"These facsimiles are all hand stenciled in pure water color and issued in a very limited edition," p. [3].

Presented by John S. Newberry.

83. Greenaway, Kate

MARIGOLD GARDEN | Pictures and Rhymes | By | KATE GREENAWAY | PRINTED IN COLOURS | By | EDMUND EVANS | LONDON | GEORGE ROUTLEDGE AND SONS | BROADWAY, LUDGATE HILL | NEW YORK: 9, LAFAYETTE PLACE

[6] 7–60 p.

a. 27.1 cm.

Green glazed pictorial boards. *Front cover:* MARIGOLD GARDEN | BY | KATE GREENAWAY, printed in white; picture of three young girls leaning over a gate, printed in colors. *Spine:* brown cloth. *Back cover:* same as front cover. All edges stained yellow. Green endpapers.

Presentation inscription: "Mrs. S. Fry From Kate Greenaway 1885," p. [1].

Presented by John S. Newberry.

b. 27.0 cm.

Green glazed pictorial boards. *Front cover:* same as item 83*a.* *Spine:* brown cloth. *Back cover:* blank. All edges stained yellow. Green endpapers.

Pen-and-ink drawing measuring 2.7 cm. of head of young girl signed "Kate Greenaway 1900," p. [1].

Presented by John S. Newberry.

84. Greenaway, Kate

MARIGOLD GARDEN | Pictures and Rhymes | by | KATE

GREENAWAY | London | FREDERICK WARNE & CO. | & New York.

[4] 5–56 p. 24.5 cm.

Olive green pictorial boards. *Front cover:* MARIGOLD | GARDEN | By | Kate Greenaway, printed in white; same picture as item 83*a*, surrounded by flowers, and floral border, printed in colors. *Spine:* olive green cloth; MARIGOLD GARDEN, stamped in black. *Back cover:* same as front cover. All edges stained pink. Pictorial endpapers.

"Copyright All Rights Reserved," verso front endpaper.

"Engraved and Printed by Edmund Evans, Ltd. at the Racquet Court Press, London," recto back endpaper.

Presented by the Friends of the Detroit Public Library.

85.   Greenaway, Kate
THE MARIGOLD PAINTING BOOK | BY | KATE | GREENAWAY | London—FREDERICK WARNE & CO.—& New York

[6] 7–33 [34–36] p. 24.6 cm.

Tan pictorial wrappers. *Front cover:* THE | MARIGOLD | PAINTING BOOK | BY | KATE | GREENAWAY | LONDON | FREDERICK WARNE & CO. | & NEW YORK, printed in green, gold, and pink; picture of girl and boy sitting on a brick fence, printed in colors; large daisies in each corner. *Spine:* THE MARIGOLD PAINTING BOOK, printed in pink. *Back cover:* advertisement for "Kate Greenaway's Picture Books." Pages [1–2] and [35–36] used as pastedowns.

"The examples of the delightful Drawings of Miss Kate Greenaway given in the following pages have been selected from her well-known children's books, notably, 'Under the Window,' 'Mother Goose,' 'A Day in a Child's Life,' etc.," p. [2].

Illustrations on pp. [4] 9, 16, 21, 28, and 33 printed in colors; the rest printed in black and white.

Presented by the Friends of the Detroit Public Library.

86.   Greenaway, Kate
MINIATURE | UNDER THE WINDOW | Pictures & Rhymes | for Children | after | KATE GREENAWAY | NEW YORK: | McLOUGHLIN BROS.

[48] p. 11.7 cm.

Gray glazed pictorial boards. *Front cover:* MINIATURE | UNDER | THE | WINDOW | AFTER | KATE GREENAWAY, printed in red; heads of two girls (not by K.G.) within circular borders, printed in colors on a yellow background. *Spine:* gray cloth. *Back cover:* same as front cover. Top edge stained yellow. Pink endpapers.

"New York Engraved and Printed by McLoughlin Bros.," p. [2].

Signature dated "April 6, 1884," verso back endpaper.

Contains black-and-white illustrations from *Under the Window.* Many of the verses, however, have been changed.

Presented by the Friends of the Detroit Public Library.

87.   Greenaway, Kate
A PAINTING | BOOK | BY | KATE GREENAWAY | With Outlines from her various Works | FOR | GIRLS & BOYS | TO PAINT | LONDON: GEORGE ROUTLEDGE & SONS | BROADWAY, LUDGATE HILL | The Pictures in this Book are Copyright.]

[3] 4–80 p.

a. 22.8 cm.

Gold cloth. *Front cover:* A PAINTING | BOOK | BY | KATE GREENAWAY | With Outlines from her various Works | FOR | GIRLS & BOYS | TO PAINT | GEORGE ROUTLEDGE & SONS, stamped in black and red; a rose, two small girls, and a boy with hoop, stamped in black; double-line at top and bottom, stamped in black. *Spine:* blank. *Back cover:* blank. White endpapers.

All illustrations, including title page and frontispiece, printed in black and white.

Contains the bookplate of Charles C. Auchincloss.

Presented by John S. Newberry.

b. 23.8 cm.

Cream-colored glazed pictorial wrappers. *Front cover:* A | PAINTING BOOK | By Kate Greenaway | GEORGE ROUT- LEDGE & SONS., printed in red and black; picture of girl paint- ing her doll, another girl watching, printed in colors. *Spine:* blank. *Back cover:* "The pictures to paint in this book are taken from *Under the Window, Kate Greenaway's Birthday Book, A Day in a Child's Life, Mother Goose, Kate Greenaway's Almanack for 1884.* Engraved and printed by Edmund Evans. Boys and girls should copy the colours from the volumes published by Messrs. George Routledge and Sons. [These Pictures are Copyright.]," printed in black.

All illustrations, including title page and frontispiece, printed in brown and white.

From the collection of Robert Partridge.

Presented by the Friends of the Detroit Public Library.

c. 24.2 cm.

Cream-colored glazed pictorial wrappers. *Front cover:* A | PAINTING BOOK | By Kate Greenaway | GEORGE ROUT- LEDGE & SONS, LIMITED, printed in black and red; same design as item 87*b*. *Spine:* blank. *Back cover:* "The pictures to paint in this book are taken from *Under the Window, Kate Green- away's Birthday Book, A Day in a Child's Life, Mother Goose.* Boys and girls should copy the colours from the volumes. Other works by Kate Greenaway are: *Marigold Garden,* . . . *The Lan- guage of Flowers.* Engraved and printed by Edmund Evans. Pub- lished by Messrs. Frederick Warne, and Company, Chandos House, Bedford Street, Strand, London. Engraved and printed by Edmund Evans, The Racquet Court Press, Swan Street, Lon- don S.E.," printed in black.

Title page and frontispiece printed in colors; other illus- trations printed in brown and white.

Presented by John S. Newberry.

88. Greenaway, Kate
   KATE GREENAWAY'S | PAINTING BOOK | WITH | OUT- LINES FROM HER VARIOUS WORKS | FOR | BOYS & GIRLS TO PAINT | LONDON | FREDERICK WARNE AND CO. | AND NEW YORK

   [6] 7–62 [63–64] p. 23.7 cm.

   Green glazed pictorial boards. *Front cover:* KATE GREEN- AWAY'S | PAINTING BOOK | LONDON | FREDERICK WARNE & CO. | & NEW YORK, printed in yellow and white; picture of girl painting her doll, another girl watching, printed in colors; stylized leaf border, printed in yellow. *Spine:* KATE GREEN- AWAY'S PAINTING BOOK, printed in beige. *Back cover:* Adver- tisement for "Kate Greenaway's Picture Books, . . . Published by Frederick Warne & Co., London: Chandos House, Bedford St., W.C. New York: 12 East 33rd Street." Pages [1–2] and [63–64] used as pastedowns.

   Illustrations on pp. [4] 9, 16, 21, 26, 35, 46, and 55 printed in colors; the rest printed in brown and white.

   Presented by Dr. and Mrs. Ned I. Chalat.

89. Greenaway, Kate
   PICTURES FOR PAINTING | By KATE GREENAWAY | WITH | OUTLINES FROM HER VARIOUS WORKS | FOR | BOYS & GIRLS TO PAINT | LONDON | FREDERICK WARNE & CO. LTD. | AND NEW YORK

   [11] l. 24.7 cm.

   Cream-colored glazed pictorial wrappers. *Front cover:* PIC-

TURES | FOR | PAINTING | By | KATE GREENAWAY | Frederick Warne and Co. Ltd., printed in brown; picture of two young girls, one holding a muff, the other a basket of flowers, surrounded by a garland of roses, printed in colors. *Spine:* blank. *Back cover:* beige board, blank. Leaves [1] and [11] used as pastedowns.

Leaves [4, 7, and 9] printed in colors and tipped in; the rest of the illustrations printed in brown and white.

From the collection of Robert Partridge.

Presented by the Friends of the Detroit Public Library.

90. Greenaway, Kate
KATE | GREENAWAY | PICTURES | FROM ORIGINALS PRESENTED BY HER | TO JOHN RUSKIN AND OTHER | PERSONAL FRIENDS | (hitherto unpublished) | With | AN APPRECIATION | By | H. M. CUNDALL, I.S.O., F.S.A. | AUTHOR OF "A HISTORY OF BRITISH WATER-COLOUR PAINTING," "BIRKET FOSTER," | "THE NORWICH SCHOOL," ETC. | LONDON | FREDERICK WARNE AND CO. LTD. | AND NEW YORK | 1921

[7] 8–11 [12–52] p. 30.5 cm.

Olive green cloth. *Front cover:* KATE | GREENAWAY | PICTURES | FROM ORIGINALS PRESENTED | BY HER TO JOHN RUSKIN | AND OTHER PERSONAL FRIENDS | WITH AN APPRECIATION BY | H. M. CUNDALL, I.S.O., F.S.A., stamped in gold and dark green. *Spine:* beige cloth; KATE GREENAWAY PICTURES, stamped in dark green. *Back cover:* blank. Fore and bottom edges uncut. Light green endpapers.

"Copyright" and "Printed in Great Britain," p. [2].

Contains the bookplate of John Gribbel.

Beige dust wrapper repeating the wording on the front cover, printed in olive green.

In publisher's case.

Presented by John S. Newberry.

91. Greenaway, Kate
GREENAWAY PICTURES | TO PAINT | NEW YORK. McLOUGHLIN BROS.

[36] p. including covers.

a. 24.5 cm.

Glazed pictorial wrappers. *Front cover:* GREENAWAY PICTURES | TO PAINT | NEW YORK. McLOUGHLIN BROS., printed in red and black; title printed on white palette containing picture of boy painting, surrounded by other illustrations by K.G., printed in colors on olive green background. *Spine:* blank.

Back cover: advertisement for "McLoughlin Bros., Latest Games and Blocks." Inside covers printed on blue.

Title taken from cover.

Advertisement for "Aunt Louisa's Big Picture Books," p. [35].

Page [3] printed in oil colors; the rest of the illustrations printed in black and white.

Presented by the Friends of the Detroit Public Library.

b. 24.2 cm.

Glazed pictorial wrappers. *Front cover:* same as item 91*a.* *Spine:* blank. *Back cover:* same as item 91*a.* Inside covers printed on white.

Title taken from cover.

Advertisement for "Aunt Louisa's Big Picture Books," p. [35].

Page [3] printed in oil colors; the rest of the illustrations printed in black and white.

92.* Greenaway, Kate

QUEEN VICTORIA'S JUBILEE GARLAND | BY | KATE GREENAWAY | ENGRAVED AND PRINTED IN COLOURS BY EDMUND EVANS | LONDON | GEORGE ROUTLEDGE AND SONS, BROADWAY, LUDGATE HILL | GLASGOW AND NEW YORK | 1887

[6] l. Oblong. 10.0 × 21.5 cm.

Cream-colored pictorial wrappers. *Front cover:* GOD SAVE OUR GRACIOUS QUEEN | LONG LIVE OUR NOBLE QUEEN | GOD SAVE THE QUEEN | QUEEN VICTORIA'S | JUBILEE | GARLAND | By KATE GREENAWAY, printed in white and red; picture of girl and boy dancing, enclosed within a circle, printed in colors. *Spine:* blank. *Back cover:* words and music to "God save our gracious Queen," printed in brown. All edges gilt. Cream-colored endpapers. Bound with pink silk tie.

Presented by John S. Newberry.

93. Greenaway, Kate

UNDER THE WINDOW | PICTURES & RHYMES | for Children | by | KATE GREENAWAY | Engraved & Printed | by | EDMUND EVANS. | LONDON: | GEORGE ROUTLEDGE & SONS, | BROADWAY, LUDGATE HILL. | NEW YORK: 416, BROOME STREET.

[6] 7–64 p. 24.4 cm.

Unbound page proofs.

*Illustrated.

92. Paper book cover.

112. "Ethelsiega and the Snail," from
Fairy Spinner.

116. Frontispiece, *Infant Amusements*, 1867,
the first known work illustrated by K.G.

"London Engraved & Printed at Racquet Court by Edmund Evans," p. [6].

"End of Contents," p. 14.

Presented by John S. Newberry.

94. Greenaway, Kate

UNDER THE WINDOW | PICTURES & RHYMES | for Children | by | KATE GREENAWAY | Engraved & Printed | by | EDMUND EVANS. | LONDON: | GEORGE ROUTLEDGE & SONS, | BROADWAY, LUDGATE HILL. | NEW YORK: 416, BROOME STREET.

a. [6] 7–64 p. 23.5 cm.

Green glazed pictorial boards. *Front cover:* UNDER | THE | WINDOW | By | Kate Greenaway, printed in red and black on green background; surrounded by a procession of children printed in white on an olive green background; border printed in green. *Spine:* blue cloth. *Back cover:* same as front cover. All edges stained yellow. Blue-black endpapers.

"London, Engraved & Printed at Racquet Court by Edmund Evans," p. [6].

"End of Contents," p. 14.

Inscription dated "Oct. 1879," p. [1].

Presented by the Friends of the Detroit Public Library.

b. [6] 7–64 p. 23.1 cm.

Green glazed pictorial boards. *Front cover:* same as item 94a. *Spine:* blue cloth. *Back cover:* same as front cover. All edges stained yellow. Dark blue endpapers.

Printer's ornaments on both sides of "Edmund Evans," p. [5] (title page).

Figure of young boy, p. [6].

Presented by John S. Newberry.

c. [6] 7–64 [65–66] p. 23.4 cm.

Green glazed pictorial boards. *Front cover:* same as item 94a. *Spine:* blue cloth. *Back cover:* same as front cover. All edges stained yellow. Blue-black endpapers.

Printer's ornaments on both sides of "Edmund Evans," p. [5] (title page).

Figure of young boy, p. [6].

"London Engraved & Printed at Racquet Court by Edmund Evans," p. [65].

Presented by the Friends of the Detroit Public Library.

95. Greenaway, Kate
UNDER THE WINDOW | PICTURES & RHYMES | for Chil-
dren | by | KATE GREENAWAY | as originally | Engraved &
Printed | by | EDMUND EVANS. | NEW YORK: | GEORGE
ROUTLEDGE & SONS, | 416 BROOME STREET.
[6] 7–64 p. 23.6 cm.
Green glazed pictorial boards. *Front cover:* same as item 94*a*.
Spine: blue cloth. *Back cover:* same as front cover. All edges
stained yellow. Blue endpapers.
"Drawn on Stone & Printed by Wemple & Company, Art
Lithographers. New York.," p. [6].
"End of Contents," p. [14].
Presented by the Friends of the Detroit Public Library.

96. Greenaway, Kate
UNDER THE WINDOW | PICTURES & RHYMES | for Chil-
dren | by | KATE GREENAWAY | London | FREDERICK
WARNE & CO. LTD. | & New York | 314.243
[4] 5–55 [56] p. 24.3 cm.
Gold glazed pictorial boards. *Front cover:* UNDER | THE |
WINDOW | By | Kate Greenaway, printed in white on gold
background; surrounded by a procession of children printed in
colors on a white background; border printed in gold. *Spine:*
beige cloth; UNDER THE WINDOW, stamped in black. *Back
cover:* same as front cover. All edges stained green. Pictorial
endpapers.
Dust jacket with same design as covers.
"Copyright all rights reserved," verso of front flyleaf.
"Printed in Great Britain," p. [4].
"Engraved and Printed by Edmund Evans, Ltd. Rose Place,
Globe Road, London, E.I.," recto of back flyleaf.
Inscription dated "May 3, 1944," recto of front flyleaf.
Contains only thirty-seven of the original forty-four illus-
trations and poems.
Presented by the Friends of the Detroit Public Library.

97. Greenaway, Kate
UNDER THE WINDOW | PICTURES & RHYMES | for Chil-
dren | after | KATE GREENAWAY | NEW YORK: |
McLOUGHLIN BROS.
[6] 7–63 [64] p. 23.6 cm.
Green glazed boards. *Front cover:* UNDER | THE | WINDOW |
After | Kate Greenaway, printed in red and black; same design

as item 94a. *Spine:* blue cloth. *Back cover:* same as front cover. All edges stained red. Blue endpapers.

"New York, Engraved & Printed by McLoughlin Bros.," p. [6].

Contains the same illustrations as item 94; however, they have been re-engraved and in some instances slightly altered. Text varies considerably.

Presented by the Friends of the Detroit Public Library.

98. Greenaway, Kate
UNDER | THE WINDOW | SERIES | THE PROUD GIRL AND OTHER | PICTURES & RHYMES | for Children | after | KATE GREENAWAY | McLOUGHLIN BROS. NEW-YORK.
41–48 p. (i.e., 8 p.) 23.5 cm.
Green paper wrappers. Title taken from front cover, printed in red and brown; with picture of proud girl walking her dog, printed in colors. *Spine:* blank. *Back cover:* McLoughlin advertisement for "Amusing and Instructive Picture Books for Children."
Separate issue of pp. 41–48 from item 97.
Presented by the Friends of the Detroit Public Library.

99. Greenaway, Kate
UNDER | THE WINDOW | SERIES | THE TEA PARTY AND OTHER | PICTURES & RHYMES | for Children | after | KATE GREENAWAY | McLOUGHLIN BROS. NEW-YORK.
17–24 p. (i.e., 8 p.) 23.5 cm.
Green paper wrappers. Title taken from front cover, printed in red and brown; picture of two girls having tea, printed in colors. *Spine:* blank. *Back cover:* McLoughlin advertisement for "Amusing and Instructive Picture Books for Children."
Separate issue of pp. 17–24 from item 97.
Presented by the Friends of the Detroit Public Library.

100. Greenaway, Kate
UNDER | THE WINDOW | SERIES | THE THREE LITTLE GIRLS AND OTHER | PICTURES & RHYMES | for Children | after | KATE GREENAWAY | McLOUGHLIN BROS. NEW-YORK.
57–64 p. (i.e., 8 p.) 23.6 cm.
Green paper wrappers. Title taken from front cover, printed in red and brown; picture of three girls sitting on a fence, printed in colors. *Spine:* blank. *Back cover:* McLoughlin advertisement for "Amusing and Instructive Picture Books for Children."

Separate issue of pp. 57–64 from item 97.
Presented by the Friends of the Detroit Public Library.

101. Greenaway, Kate
UNDER | THE WINDOW | SERIES | THE THREE LITTLE
SAILORS AND OTHER | PICTURES & RHYMES | for Children |
after | KATE GREENAWAY | McLOUGHLIN BROS. NEW-
YORK.
49–56 p. (i.e., 8 p.) 23.6 cm.
Green paper wrappers. Title taken from front cover, printed
in red and brown; picture of three children in two row boats,
printed in colors. *Spine:* blank. *Back cover:* McLoughlin advertisement for "Amusing and Instructive Picture Books for Children."
Separate issue of pp. 49–56 from item 97.
Presented by the Friends of the Detroit Public Library.

102. Greenaway, Kate
UNDER | THE WINDOW | SERIES | TOMMY TODDYHIGH
AND OTHER | PICTURES & RHYMES | for Children | after |
KATE GREENAWAY | McLOUGHLIN BROS. NEW-YORK.
33–40 p. (i.e., 8 p.) 23.6 cm.
Green paper wrappers. Title taken from front cover, printed
in red and brown; picture of three children playing on a bridge,
printed in colors. *Spine:* blank. *Back cover:* McLoughlin's advertisement for "Amusing and Instructive Picture Books for Children."
Separate issue of pp. 33–40 from item 97.
Presented by the Friends of the Detroit Public Library.

103. Haile, Ellen
THREE BROWN BOYS | AND | OTHER HAPPY CHILDREN.
| BY ELLEN HAILE. | CASSELL & COMPANY, LIMITED | NEW
YORK, LONDON AND PARIS
[4] [i] ii–iv [5] 6–228 [4] p. 21.2 cm.
Glazed pictorial boards. *Front cover:* 3 BROWN BOYS | &
OTHER HAPPY | CHILDREN | CASSELL & COMPANY, LIM-
ITED. | NEW YORK, LONDON, PARIS & MELBOURNE. |
COPYRIGHT 1886 BY O. M. DUNHAM., printed in orange, red
and black; picture by K.G. of three boys in long overcoats and
hats, printed in colors. *Spine:* 3 | BROWN | BOYS, printed in
yellow; publisher's monogram, printed in black. *Back cover:* 3
BROWN BOYS | AND | OTHER HAPPY CHILDREN | H.
BENCKE, LITH. N.Y., printed in red and black; picture of small

child holding a balloon and young girl with an umbrella, printed in colors. White endpapers.

"Copyright 1879, By O. M. Dunham" and "Press of W. L. Mershon & Co., Rahway, N.J.," p. [4] at beginning.

"New Books for the Young Folks, selected from the Catalogue of Cassell & Company, Limited," pp. [1–4] at end.

Signature dated "Nov. 19, 1887," front flyleaf.

Contains black-and-white illustrations signed "K.G.," frontispiece and p. 214, and unsigned black-and-white illustrations by K.G., pp. 20, 24, 25, and 29.

Presented by the Friends of the Detroit Public Library.

104. Haile, Ellen

THREE BROWN BOYS | AND | OTHER HAPPY CHILDREN. | BY ELLEN HAILE. | CASSELL, PETTER & GALPIN, | NEW YORK, LONDON AND PARIS.

[4] [i] ii–iv [5] 6–228 p. 21.4 cm.

Pictorial boards. *Front cover:* 3 | BROWN | BOYS | GASSELL (*sic*), PETTER, | GALPIN & CO. | & | OTHER HAPPY CHILDREN | DONALDSON BROTHERS, FIVE POINTS, NEW YORK, printed in red and black; picture by K.G. of three boys in long overcoats and hats, printed in colors. *Spine:* brown cloth. *Back cover:* advertisement for *Bessie Bradford's Secret* by Joanna H. Mathews. White endpapers.

"Copyright, 1879, by O. M. Dunham" and "New York: J. J. Little & Co., Printers, 10 to 20 Astor Place," p. [4] at beginning.

Contains black-and-white illustrations signed "K.G.," frontispiece and p. 214, and unsigned black-and-white illustrations by K.G., pp. 20, 24, 25, and 29.

Presented by the Friends of the Detroit Public Library.

105. Haile, Ellen

THE | TWO GRAY GIRLS | AND | THEIR OPPOSITE NEIGHBORS. | BY | ELLEN HAILE, | AUTHOR OF "THREE BROWN BOYS." | WITH ILLUSTRATIONS | BY | KATE GREENAWAY, M. E. EDWARDS AND OTHERS. | CASSELL, PETTER, GALPIN & CO., | NEW YORK, LONDON AND PARIS.

[7] 8–258 p.

"Copyright, 1880, by O. M. Dunham" and "New York: J. J. Little & Co., Printers, 10 to 20 Astor Place," p. [4].

Contains three black-and-white illustrations signed "K.G.," pp. [2] (frontispiece), 12, and 46.

a. 21.1 cm.

Beige boards. *Front cover:* TWO GRAY GIRLS | CASSELL,

PETTER, GALPIN & CO. LONDON, PARIS & NEW YORK, printed in red and black; picture by K.G. of two girls in winter attire, printed in colors. Spine: green cloth. *Back cover:* advertisement by Cassell, Petter, Galpin & Co. for new books. All edges stained beige. White endpapers.

Presented by the Friends of the Detroit Public Library.

b. 21.3 cm.

Brown cloth. *Front cover:* TWO GRAY GIRLS, stamped in gold and black; picture by K.G. of two girls in winter attire, stamped in gold; triple-line border, stamped in black. *Spine:* TWO | GRAY | GIRLS, stamped in gold. *Back cover:* double-line border and decorative device in center, blind-stamped. Brown endpapers.

106. Haile, Ellen

THE | TWO GRAY GIRLS | AND | THEIR OPPOSITE NEIGHBORS. | BY | ELLEN HAILE, | AUTHOR OF "THREE BROWN BOYS." | WITH ILLUSTRATIONS | BY | KATE GREENAWAY, M. E. EDWARDS AND OTHERS. | CASSELL & COMPANY, Limited, | NEW YORK, LONDON & PARIS.

[5] 8–256 [2] p. (i.e., 256 p.) 21.3 cm.

Blue cloth. *Front cover:* same as item 105*b*. *Spine:* same as item 105*b*. *Back cover:* blank. White endpapers.

Dedication, "Copyright 1880, by O. M. Dunham," and "Press of W. L. Mershon & Co., Rahway, N.J.," p. [4].

"New Books for the Young Folks, selected from the Catalogue of Cassell & Company, Limited," pp. [1–2] at end.

Contains three black-and-white illustrations signed "K.G.," pp. [2] (frontispiece), 12, and 46.

Presented by Mrs. Elizabeth Halfert.

107. Handford, Thomas W., ed.

OUR GIRLS. | Stories and Poems for Little Girls, | BY | LAURIE LORING, LOUISA M. ALCOTT, H. B. HUDSON, OLIVE THORNE, | AND CELIA THAXTER. | EDITED BY THOMAS W. HANDFORD | BEAUTIFULLY ILLUSTRATED. | CHICAGO, NEW YORK, SAN FRANCISCO: | BELFORD, CLARKE & CO.| 1890.

[6] 7–206 [2] p. 23.9 cm.

Glazed pictorial boards. *Front cover:* OUR GIRLS | Chicago, New York | and San Francisco. | BELFORD, | CLARKE & CO. | THE HENDERSON-ACHERT LITH. CO. CIN. O., printed in red and black; picture of two girls in circular frame with large rose at bottom, printed in colors. *Spine:* brown cloth. *Back cover:*

advertisement for *Belford's Annual 1889–90* and *Belford's Magazine*. White endpapers.

"Copyright 1886, Belford, Clarke & Co.," p. [4].

Contains one unsigned black-and-white illustration by K.G., p. [3] (title page).

108.* Harte, Bret

THE QUEEN | OF | THE PIRATE ISLE | BY | BRET HARTE | ILLUSTRATED BY KATE GREENAWAY | ENGRAVED AND PRINTED BY EDMUND EVANS | LONDON: CHATTO AND WINDUS | 214 PICCADILLY.

[9] 10–16 [17–64] p. 21.6 cm.

Olive green imitation morocco boards. *Front cover:* THE | QUEEN | OF THE | PIRATE ISLE | BY | BRET HARTE | ILLUS-TRATED BY | KATE GREENAWAY, stamped in red and navy blue; picture of three children on a "boat" (illustration from p. 13) and single-line border, stamped in navy blue. *Spine:* blank. *Back cover:* single-line border, blind-stamped. Blue endpapers.

Proof copy. Page [7], "List of Illustrations," contains page numbers only up to p. 16. Printed text and illustrations also only to p. 16. Pages [17–64] blank.

The following blank pages contain drawings by K.G. in the manner of medieval initials and border designs: watercolor initial signed "K.G.," p. [19]; watercolor initial and ornament signed "K.G.," p. [21]; watercolor border and six pencil ornaments, p. [23]; watercolor initial signed "K.G.," p. [25]; four pen-and-ink initials, p. [27]; six watercolor initials signed "K.G.," p. [29]; watercolor initial signed "K.G.," p. [31]; four watercolor initials signed "K.G.," p. [33]; one watercolor initial and three pen-and-ink initials, p. [35]; three pencil initials, p. [37]; pen-and-ink border design, p. [39]; and pencil outline of initial, p. [41].

Presented by John S. Newberry.

109. Harte, Bret

THE QUEEN | OF | THE PIRATE ISLE | BY | BRET HARTE | ILLUSTRATED BY KATE GREENAWAY | ENGRAVED AND PRINTED BY EDMUND EVANS | LONDON: CHATTO AND WINDUS | 214, PICCADILLY.

[9] 10–58 p.

a. 21.4 cm.

Beige cloth. *Front cover:* The Queen | OF THE | Pirate Isle | BY | BRET HARTE | ILLUSTRATED | BY | KATE GREENAWAY, stamped in gold and black; picture of three children on a "boat"

*Illustrated.

(illustration from p. 13), stamped in colors; double-line border, stamped in gold. *Spine:* The | Queen | of the | Pirate | Isle | BY | BRET | HARTE | K.G., stamped in black. *Back cover:* same wording as front cover, with picture of three children (illustration from p. 16), stamped in colors. All edges stained gold. White endpapers.

Presented by John S. Newberry.

b. 21.5 cm.

Beige cloth. *Front cover:* same as item 109*a. Spine:* same as item 109*a. Back cover:* same as item 109*a.* All edges gilt. Blue endpapers.

Presented by John S. Newberry.

110. Harte, Bret

THE QUEEN | OF | THE PIRATE ISLE | BY | BRET HARTE | ILLUSTRATED BY KATE GREENAWAY | ENGRAVED AND PRINTED BY EDMUND EVANS | BOSTON AND NEW YORK: | HOUGHTON, MIFFLIN AND COMPANY. | The Riverside Press, Cambridge. | 1887.

[9] 10–58 p. 21.5 cm.

Beige cloth. *Front cover:* same as item 109*a. Spine:* same as item 109*a. Back cover:* same as item 109*a.* All edges gilt. Blue endpapers.

"Copyright, 1886. By Houghton, Mifflin & Co. All Rights Reserved.," p. [6].

Presented by the Friends of the Detroit Public Library.

111. Harte, Bret

THE QUEEN | OF | THE PIRATE ISLE | BY | BRET HARTE | ILLUSTRATED BY KATE GREENAWAY | FREDERICK WARNE & CO. LTD. | LONDON & NEW YORK

Two sheets of seventy-two uncut pages plus designs for the dust jacket.

"This book is copyright in all countries signatory to the Berne Convention. Frederick Warne & Co., Ltd., London. Reissued 1955. Printed in Great Britain by Edmund Evans Ltd. London. 966.456," verso of title page.

From the collection of Robert Partridge.

Presented by the Friends of the Detroit Public Library.

112.* Hill, Miranda

THE FAIRY SPINNER | AND | "OUT OF DATE OR NOT?" | BY | MIRANDA HILL | NEW EDITION | London: | MARCUS

*Illustrated.

WARD & CO., LIMITED | ORIEL HOUSE, FARRINGDON STREET | AND AT BELFAST AND NEW YORK

[9] 10–224 p. 16.3 cm.

Brown cloth. *Front cover:* The | FAIRY SPINNER | Illustrated by | KATE | GREENAWAY, stamped in gold and black; picture of woman with jug in hand looking at the sky, and birds, stamped in gold and black. *Spine:* The | Fairy | Spinner | by | MIRANDA HILL | MARCUS WARD | & CO LIMITED, stamped in gold and black; picture of princess holding her skirts, stamped in gold. *Back cover:* double-line border, blind-stamped. Beige endpapers.

"Marcus Ward and Co., Royal Ulster Works, Belfast," p. 224.

Two leaves containing a colored frontispiece and added decorative title page inserted between pp. [4 and 5]; four other black-and-white illustrations inserted between pp. 18 and 19, 80 and 81, 128 and 129, and 176 and 177.

113. Hodder, Edwin

THE | ROUND ROBIN: | A GATHERING OF | Fact, Fiction, Incident, and Adventure. | EDITED BY | OLD MERRY. | WITH ORIGINAL ILLUSTRATIONS BY BIRKET FOSTER AND J. D. WATSON, | Printed in Colours by Edmund Evans, AND NUMEROUS WOODCUTS BY H. D. FRISTON, J. A. PASQUIER, | W. G. R. BROWNE, &c., &c. | LONDON: | FREDERICK WARNE AND CO., | BEDFORD STREET, COVENT GARDEN. | NEW YORK: SCRIBNER, WELFORD, AND ARMSTRONG.

[i]-viii [1] 2–960 p. 20.8 cm.

Red cloth. *Front cover:* The | ROUND ROBIN | EDITED BY | OLD MERRY, stamped in black and gold; decorative design of flowers in each corner, stamped in gold; five-line border, stamped in black. *Spine:* The | ROUND ROBIN | OLD MERRY | ILLUSTRATED | F. WARNE & CO, stamped in black and gold; decorative design of flowers stamped in black and gold. *Back cover:* WARNE & CO BEDFORD ST. COVENT GARDEN, blind-stamped in circle in center; triple-line border, blind-stamped. All edges gilt. White endpapers.

"Unwin Brothers, Printers, London and Chilworth," pp. [ii] and 960.

Frontispiece and twenty-six illustrations inserted.

Contains two black-and-white illustrations signed "Kate Greenaway," following pp. 286 and 602.

Presented by the Friends of the Detroit Public Library.

114. Jerrold, Alice

A CRUISE | IN | THE ACORN | BY | ALICE JERROLD | (MRS.

ADOLPHE SMITH.) | WITH SIX ILLUSTRATIONS, IN GOLD AND COLORS | "Acorns which the winds have scattered | Future navies may provide!" | London: | MARCUS WARD & CO., 67 & 68, CHANDOS STREET, COVENT GARDEN | AND ROYAL ULSTER WORKS, BELFAST | 1875

[7] 8–140 [4] p. 20.7 cm.

Green cloth, beveled edges. *Front cover:* A | CRUISE | IN THE | ACORN, stamped in gold; decorative design stamped in black; picture of flowers, printed in colors on glazed paper, pasted on left-hand side of cover; triple-line border, stamped in black and gold. *Spine:* A | CRUISE | IN THE | ACORN | MARCUS | WARD | & CO., stamped in gold and black; decorative design, stamped in black and gold. *Back cover:* trellis design and single-line border, blind-stamped. Dark blue endpapers.

"Marcus Ward & Co., Printers, Royal Ulster Works, Belfast," p. 140.

"New Works & New Editions, Published by Marcus Ward & Co.," pp. [1–4] at end.

Contains six unsigned illustrations by K.G. printed in colors on stiff glazed paper and mounted within a black-and-white ornamental border, pp. [2, 38, 61, 91, 121, and 128].

Presented by the Friends of the Detroit Public Library.

115.   KING | Christmas | after | Caldecott | Kate Greenaway | Miss Cassella | & others. | New York | Dodd Mead & Company | Publishers. | COPYRIGHT 1881, BY DODD, MEAD & COMPANY.

[3] 4–32 p. 24.0 cm.

Beige glazed boards. *Front cover:* KING | Dodd Mead & Company | New York | CHRISTMAS, printed in black; picture by K.G. of young girl in winter attire holding a holly branch, printed in colors. *Spine:* beige cloth. *Back cover:* CADWELL LITH. CO. NY, printed in black; picture of bearded man waving and half of an evergreen tree, printed in colors. Decorative orange and white endpapers.

Contains colored illustrations signed "K.G.," pp. 18–19, and unsigned colored illustrations by K.G., pp. 20–21.

Presented by the Friends of the Detroit Public Library.

116.* Kingston, William H. G.

INFANT AMUSEMENTS; | OR, | HOW TO MAKE A NURSERY HAPPY. | WITH | PRACTICAL HINTS TO PARENTS AND NURSES | ON | THE MORAL AND PHYSICAL TRAIN-

*Illustrated.

ING OF CHILDREN. | BY | WILLIAM H. G. KINGSTON. | LONDON: | GRIFFITH AND FARRAN, | CORNER OF ST. PAUL'S CHURCHYARD. | MDCCCLXVII.

[2] [iii] iv–xviii [1] 2–183 [184] [3] 4–32 p. 18.1 cm.

Red cloth. *Front cover:* INFANT | AMUSEMENTS, outlined by decorative ornament stamped in gold; decorative border, stamped in black. *Spine:* INFANT | AMUSEMENTS, outlined by decorative ornament stamped in gold; LONDON. | GRIFFITH & FARRAN, stamped in gold. *Back cover:* same decorative border as front cover, blind-stamped. Brown endpapers.

"A catalogue of new & popular works, and of books suitable for presents and school prizes. Published by Griffith and Farran," pp. [1–3] 4–32 at end. Catalogue dated "5M.5.79."

Contains black-and-white frontispiece signed "Kate Greenaway," p. [2] at the beginning.

Presented by John S. Newberry.

117. Knox, Kathleen

FAIRY GIFTS; | OR, | A WALLET OF WONDERS. | BY KATHLEEN KNOX, | AUTHOR OF 'FATHER TIMES'S (*sic*) STORY BOOK.' | ILLUSTRATIONS BY KATE GREENAWAY. | GRIFFITH AND FARRAN, | SUCCESSORS TO NEWBURY AND HARRIS, | WEST CORNER OF ST. PAUL'S CHURCH-YARD, LONDON. | E. P. DUTTON & CO., NEW YORK.

a. [5] 6–128 p. 17.1 cm.

Gray glazed pictorial boards. *Front cover:* FAIRY GIFTS | Dupuy & Fils. Paris & London | ILLUSTRATED BY KATE GREENAWAY | GRIFFITH & FARRAN E. P. DUTTON & CO. | LONDON NEW-YORK, printed in white and black; picture of the Fairy Rubinetta holding her broom and looking in the distance, printed in colors. *Spine:* blue cloth. *Back cover:* gray board, blank. All edges stained yellow. Gray and white floral-patterned endpapers.

"Morrison and Gibb, Edinburgh, Printers to Her Majesty's Stationery Office" and "5 M.-12/82-S & S," p. 128.

Presented by the Friends of the Detroit Public Library.

b. [5] 6–128 [3] 4–31 [32] p. 17.1 cm.

Yellow glazed pictorial boards. *Front cover:* same as item 117a. *Spine:* pink cloth; FAIRY GIFTS | GRIFFITH | AND | FARRAN | LONDON, stamped in black. *Back cover:* gray board; publisher's device, printed in black. All edges stained yellow. Green and white decorative endpapers.

"Morrison and Gibb, Edinburgh, Printers to Her Majesty's Stationery Office," p. 128.

"A Catalogue of Books for the Young of all ages . . . published by Griffith and Farran," pp. [1–3] 4–31 [32] at end. Catalogue dated "10M.10.82."

From the collection of Robert Partridge.

Presented by the Friends of the Detroit Public Library.

    c. [5] 6–128 [2] 3–30 [31–32] p. 17.0 cm.

Gray glazed pictorial boards. *Front cover:* same as item 117*a*. *Spine:* red cloth, same as item 117*b*. *Back cover:* gray boards, blank. All edges stained yellow. Green and white floral endpapers.

"Morrison and Gibb, Edinburgh, Printers to Her Majesty's Stationery Office" and "5M.-12/82-S. & S.," p. 128.

"A Catalogue of Books for the Young . . . Published by Griffith, Farran, Okeden, & Welsh," pp. [1–2] 3–30 [31] at end. Catalogue dated "20M. 9.84.G.C. & Co."

Presented by the Friends of the Detroit Public Library.

118. Kringle, George

    SOME LITTLE PEOPLE | BY | GEORGE KRINGLE | ILLUS-TRATED | NEW YORK | DODD, MEAD & COMPANY | PUB-LISHERS

    [5] 8–128 p. (i.e., 126 p.) 16.8 cm.

Blue cloth. *Front cover:* LITTLE PEOPLE, stamped in gold; two pictures, one of boy holding a bouquet of flowers in one hand and a letter in the other, one of girl holding a basket of flowers, each printed in colors on stiff paper and pasted to the cover; assortment of fans and feathers, stamped in black and gold. *Spine:* leaf design, stamped in gold. *Back cover:* triple-line border, blind-stamped. Cream-colored endpapers.

"Copyright, 1881, by Dodd, Mead & Company," p. [4].

Contains black-and-white illustrations signed "K.G.," pp. [15, 23, 31, 39, and 67], and an unsigned black-and-white illustration by K.G., p. [75].

Presented by the Friends of the Detroit Public Library.

119. Lablache, Fanny

    STARLIGHT STORIES | TOLD TO | BRIGHT EYES AND LISTENING EARS | BY | FANNY LABLACHE | With Illus-trations by K. Greenaway | LONDON: | GRIFFITH, FARRAN, BROWNE & CO., LTD. | 35 BOW STREET, COVENT GARDEN | All Rights Reserved

    [15] 16–190 p. 17.0 cm.

Gold cloth. *Front cover:* STARLIGHT | STORIES, stamped in black; flowers, leaves, and butterflies, stamped in colors; de-corative top and bottom border, stamped in colors. *Spine:*

STARLIGHT | STORIES | GRIFFITH FARRAN & Co., stamped in black; flower, stamped in colors. *Back cover:* blank. White endpapers.

"Turnbull & Spears, Printers, Edinburgh," p. 190.

Presentation bookplate dated "July 31, 1898," recto front flyleaf.

Presented by the Friends of the Detroit Public Library.

120. Lang, Andrew

THE LIBRARY | BY | ANDREW LANG | WITH A CHAPTER ON | MODERN ENGLISH ILLUSTRATED BOOKS BY | AUSTIN DOBSON |London |MACMILLAN & CO. |1881 |The right of reproduction is reserved.

[ix] x–[xvi] [1] 2–184 [8] p. 18.0 cm.

Blue cloth. *Front cover:* ART AT HOME | THE | LIBRARY | A. LANG, stamped in black; publisher's monogram, stamped in black. *Spine:* THE LIBRARY A. LANG, stamped in black. *Back cover:* ART | AT | HOME | SERIES, stamped in black. Gray endpapers.

Publisher's advertisements, pp. [1–8] at end.

Contains black-and-white illustrations signed "K.G.," p. 122.

Presented by the Friends of the Detroit Public Library.

121. Lang, Andrew

THE LIBRARY | BY | ANDREW LANG | WITH A CHAPTER ON | MODERN ENGLISH ILLUSTRATED BOOKS BY | AUSTIN DOBSON | SECOND EDITION | London | MACMILLAN & CO. | AND NEW YORK | 1892 | All rights reserved

[2] [ix] x–[xxii] [1] 2–192 p. 25.8 cm.

Brown cloth. *Front cover:* pile of four books in center, stamped in gold. *Spine:* THE | LIBRARY | ANDREW | LANG | MACMILLAN & Co., stamped in gold. *Back cover:* blank. All edges uncut. White endpapers.

"Three hundred copies of this large paper edition were printed, November 1892. No. 216," p. [ii].

Woodcut signed "K.G.," p. 122.

Presented by Mrs. Frank J. Hecker.

122. LITTLE | SUNBEAM STORIES. | COMPRISING: | LITTLE SCHOOLMATES, | LITTLE PLAYFELLOWS, | LITTLE CHATTERER. | CASSELL, PETTER, GALPIN & CO., | NEW YORK, LONDON, AND PARIS.

[iv] [6] 7–[96]; [4] 5–96; [6] 7–[96] p. 20.5 cm.

Brown cloth. *Front cover:* Little | SUNBEAM | STORIES, stamped in gold; picture of a sunrise and daisies, stamped in black and gold. *Spine:* LITTLE | SUNBEAM | STORIES, stamped in gold; daisies, stamped in black. *Back cover:* double-line border and decorative design in center, blind-stamped. Yellow end-papers.

"Copyright, 1880, by O. M. Dunham" and "Press of J. J. Little & Co., Nos. 10 to 20 Astor Place, New York:," p. [2] at beginning.

Each story has its own title page and pagination.

Contains black-and-white illustrations signed by K.G., pp. [3] 13, 19, 59, 62, 67, 74, and 80 (first pagination), 7, 36, and 38 (second pagination), and unsigned black-and-white illustrations by K.G., pp. 26 and 65 (first pagination) and [3] (third pagination).

123. Locker, Frederick
LONDON LYRICS | BY | FREDERICK LOCKER | LONDON | 1881
[ix] x [1] 2–108 [109–10] p. 22.8 cm.
Dark red cloth. *Front cover:* triple-line border, stamped in gold. *Spine:* LONDON | LYRICS | LOCKER, stamped in gold. *Back cover:* same as front cover. All edges uncut. White end-papers.
"Chiswick Press:—C. Whittingham and Co., Tooks Court, Chancery Lane," p. [6].
Contains black-and-white illustration signed "K.G." between pp. 102 and 103.
From the collection of Robert Partridge.
Presented by the Friends of the Detroit Public Library.

124. Locker, Frederick
THE POEMS | OF | FREDERICK LOCKER | AUTHORIZED EDITION | NEW YORK | WHITE, STOKES, & ALLEN | 1884
[4] [i]-[viii] [1] 8–262 [4] p. (i.e., 272 p.) 19.5 cm.
Light green cloth, beveled edges. *Front cover:* POEMS. | FREDERICK LOCKER, stamped in dark green; illustration from Frederick Locker's bookplate designed by K.G., stamped in gold. *Spine:* POEMS | OF | FRED'K | LOCKER | WHITE, | STOKES, | & ALLEN, stamped in gold. *Back cover:* blank. All edges gilt. Green and white floral endpapers.

125. Locker-Lampson, Frederick
LONDON LYRICS | BY | FREDERICK LOCKER LAMPSON | WITH INTRODUCTION AND NOTES | BY AUSTIN DOBSON | London | MACMILLAN AND CO., LIMITED | NEW YORK: THE MACMILLAN COMPANY | 1904 | All rights reserved

[vi] vii–xxv [1] 2–196 [1]–4 p. 14.6 cm.

Rebound copy.

Publisher's advertisements, pp. [1]–4 at end.

Illustration of Frederick Locker's bookplate designed by K.G., title page.

126. Loftie, William John

LONDON | AFTERNOONS | CHAPTERS ON THE SOCIAL LIFE, | ARCHITECTURE, AND RECORDS | OF THE GREAT CITY AND ITS |NEIGHBOURHOOD |BY |W. J. LOFTIE, B.A., F.S.A., F.Z.S. | AUTHOR OF "A HISTORY OF LONDON," "WINDSOR," AND | "THE AUTHORISED GUIDE TO THE TOWER": AND EDITOR OF | "THE ORIENT GUIDE" | WITH UPWARDS OF SIXTY ILLUSTRATIONS | CASSELL AND COMPANY, LIMITED | LONDON | BRENTANOS | NEW YORK | 1902

[2] [i]–xii [1] 2–292 p. 19.5 cm.

Rebound copy.

Contains black-and-white illustration, "John of Berkhampstead, Abbot of St. Albans," by K.G., between pp. 110 and 111 (M. H. Spielmann and G. S. Layard, *Kate Greenaway* [London, 1905], p. 47).

127. Loftie, William John

ORIENT LINE GUIDE | CHAPTERS FOR TRAVELLERS BY SEA AND BY LAND | ILLUSTRATED. | THE THIRD EDITION, RE-WRITTEN, WITH MAPS AND PLANS. | EDITED FOR THE MANAGERS OF THE LINE | BY | W. J. LOFTIE, B.A., F.S.A., | AUTHOR OF "A HISTORY OF LONDON," "WINDSOR," "AUTHORISED | GUIDE TO THE TOWER," ETC., ETC. | PRICE 2/6. | London: | SAMPSON LOW, MARSTON, SEARLE, & RIVINGTON, | LIMITED, | ST. DUNSTAN'S HOUSE, FETTER LANE. | EDWARD STANFORD, 26 & 27, COCKSPUR STREET, S.W. | 1888. | Entered at Stationers' Hall.] [All Rights Reserved.

xxxvii [2] [1] 2–439 p. 20.4 cm.

Dark blue glazed boards. *Front cover:* ORIENT | GUIDE, stamped in gold; crown, stamped in gold; triple-line border, blind-stamped. *Spine:* ORIENT GUIDE, with crown, stamped in gold. *Back cover:* same as front cover, blind-stamped. All edges stained red. Pagination begins with front pastedown.

Contains black-and-white illustration signed "K.G.," p. [viii].

Presented by John S. Newberry.

128. Loftie, William John
ORIENT LINE GUIDE | CHAPTERS FOR TRAVELLERS BY
SEA AND BY LAND | ILLUSTRATED. | THE THIRD EDITION,
RE-WRITTEN, WITH MAPS AND PLANS. | EDITED FOR THE
MANAGERS OF THE LINE | BY | W. J. LOFTIE, B.A., F.S.A., |
AUTHOR OF "A HISTORY OF LONDON," "WINDSOR,"
"AUTHORISED | GUIDE TO THE TOWER," ETC., ETC. |
PRICE 2/6. | London: | SAMPSON LOW, MARSTON, SEARLE,
& RIVINGTON, | LIMITED, | ST. DUNSTAN'S HOUSE, FET-
TER LANE. | EDWARD STANFORD, 26 & 27, COCKSPUR
STREET, S.W. | 1889. | Entered at Stationers' Hall.] [All Rights
Reserved.

[1] xxxvii [2] [1] 2–439 p. 20.2 cm.

Dark blue glazed boards. *Front cover:* same as item 127. *Spine:*
same as item 127. *Back cover:* same as item 127. All edges stained
red. Advertisement, front pastedown; pagination ends with
back pastedown.

Contains black-and-white illustration signed "K.G.," p. [x].

Presented by the Friends of the Detroit Public Library.

129. Loftie, William John
ORIENT LINE GUIDE | CHAPTERS FOR TRAVELLERS BY
SEA AND BY LAND | ILLUSTRATED. | THE FOURTH EDI-
TION, REVISED, WITH MAPS AND PLANS. | EDITED FOR
THE MANAGERS OF THE LINE | BY | W. J. LOFTIE, B.A.,
F.S.A., | AUTHOR OF "A HISTORY OF LONDON,"
"WINDSOR," "AUTHORISED | GUIDE TO THE TOWER,"
ETC., ETC. | PRICE 2/6. | London: | SAMPSON LOW,
MARSTON, SEARLE, & RIVINGTON, | LIMITED, | ST.
DUNSTAN'S HOUSE, FETTER LANE. | EDWARD STAN-
FORD, 26 & 27 COCKSPUR STREET, S.W. | 1890 | Entered at
Stationers' Hall.] [All Rights Reserved.

xliii [1] 2–439 p. 20.2 cm.

Dark blue glazed boards. *Front cover:* same as item 127. *Spine:*
same as item 127. *Back cover:* same as item 127. All edges stained
red. Pagination begins with front pastedown.

Contains black-and-white illustration signed "K.G.," p. [x].

Presented by the Friends of the Detroit Public Library.

130. Martin, William
THE | LITTLE FOLK'S | OUT AND ABOUT | BOOK. | BY |
CHATTY CHEERFUL. | CASSELL & COMPANY, LIMITED: |
LONDON, PARIS & NEW YORK. | [ALL RIGHTS RESERVED.]

[7] 8–176 [1]2–[8] p. 24.5 cm.

Brown cloth. *Front cover:* THE | LITTLE FOLK'S | OUT AND

ABOUT | BOOK, stamped in black and gold; picture of young girl in winter attire carrying a basket and umbrella, stamped in black and gold; picture of girl and boy going to school, several children standing by a fence, and a boy trying to fetch an open umbrella from the water, stamped in black and gold. *Spine:* LIT-TLE | FOLK'S | OUT | AND | ABOUT | BOOK, stamped in gold; picture of girl on swing, stamped in black and gold. *Back cover:* decorative device in center and triple-line border, blind-stamped. All edges gilt. White endpapers.

"Cassell & Company, Limited, Belle Sauvage Works, London, E.C.," p. 176.

"A Selected List of Cassell & Company's Publications," pp. [1–8] at end. Code "14L—884," bottom of p. [1] at end.

Contains black-and-white illustrations signed "K.G.," pp. 39 and 87, and an unsigned black-and-white illustration by K.G., p. 50.

Presented by John S. Newberry.

131. Matéaux, Clara L.

CHATS | FOR | SMALL CHATTERERS. | CASSELL PETTER & GALPIN: | LONDON, PARIS & NEW YORK.

[6] 7–188 [189] p. 16.9 cm.

Red cloth. *Front cover:* CHATS FOR SMALL | CHATTERERS, stamped in black and gold; picture of young girl with roses, young boy, lamb, and dog, printed in colors on glazed paper and pasted on center surrounded by decorative design, stamped in black and gold. *Spine:* CHATS | FOR | SMALL | CHAT- | TERERS, outlined by decorative design stamped in gold; decorative design, stamped in black and gold. *Back cover:* triple-line border, blind-stamped. Pale yellow endpapers.

"The Cosy Corner Series," p. [5].

Although unsigned and unidentified, the black-and-white illustrations on pages [68] and [108] look very much like the early work of K.G.

132. Matéaux, Clara L.

WOODLAND ROMANCES; | OR, | FABLES AND FANCIES. | BY | C. L. MATÉAUX, | Author of "Home Chat," "Around and About Old England," &c. | CASSELL PETTER & GALPIN: | LONDON, PARIS & NEW YORK.

[v] vi–[ix] 10–192 [1] 2–[8] p. 21.5 cm.

Green cloth. *Front cover:* WOODLAND | ROMANCES | OR | FABLES & | FANCIES, stamped in gold and black; picture of cormorant standing on the shore looking at fishes whose heads are sticking out of the water, stamped in black and gold. *Spine:*

WOOdLANd | ROMANCES | ILLUSTRATED, stamped in gold; with decorative design stamped in black and gold. *Back cover:* decorative device in center and single-line border, blind-stamped. All edges gilt. White endpapers.

"Cassell Petter & Galpin, Belle Sauvage Works, London, E.C.," p. 192.

"A Selected List of Messrs. Cassell Petter & Galpin's Publications," pp. [1–8] at end.

Contains unsigned black-and-white illustrations by K.G., pp. 18 and 19.

Presented by John S. Newberry.

133. Mavor, William
The | English Spelling-Book | ACCOMPANIED BY | A PRO-GRESSIVE SERIES | OF | EASY AND FAMILIAR LESSONS | BY | WILLIAM MAVOR, LL.D. | ILLUSTRATED BY KATE GREENAWAY | ENGRAVED AND PRINTED BY EDMUND EVANS | LONDON | GEORGE ROUTLEDGE AND SONS | BROADWAY, LUDGATE HILL | NEW YORK: 9 LAFAYETTE PLACE | 1885.

[9] 10–108 p. 17.6 cm.

Gray boards. *Front cover:* The English | Spelling-Book | BY | WILLIAM MAVOR LL.D. | ILLUSTRATED BY KATE GREENAWAY | LONDON | GEORGE ROUTLEDGE AND SONS | BROADWAY, LUDGATE HILL | NEW YORK: 9 LAFAYETTE PLACE, printed in black and orange; picture of young woman holding the hand of young boy, printed in orange and black. *Spine:* The English Spelling-Book., printed in black and orange. *Back cover:* same as front cover. All edges speckled blue. White endpapers.

"London: Engraved and printed by Edmund Evans, Racquet Court, Fleet Street," p. [4].

"Engraved and Printed by Edmund Evans, Racquet Court, Fleet Street, E.C.," p. 108.

All illustrations printed in brown.

Presented by John S. Newberry.

134. Miller, Nancy Minerva Haynes
MOTHER TRUTH'S | MELODIES. | COMMON SENSE FOR CHILDREN. | A KINDERGARTEN. | BY | MRS. E. P. MILLER, | AUTHOR OF "A FATHER'S ADVICE: A BOOK FOR EVERY BOY," AND "A MOTHER'S | ADVICE: A BOOK FOR EVERY GIRL." | NEARLY 400 ILLUSTRATIONS. | NEW AND EN-LARGED EDITION. | SPRINGFIELD, MASS. | BAY STATE PUBLISHING CO. | 1885.

[ii] [7] 8–296 [ii] p. 18.3 cm.

Red cloth. *Front cover:* MOTHER TRUTH'S | MELODIES, stamped in black and gold; unsigned illustration by K.G. of three maidens curtsying, stamped in black; decorative design of elves and little people along left-hand side and bottom and double-line border, stamped in black. *Spine:* MOTHER | TRUTHS | MELODIES, stamped in black on gold; decorative design, stamped in black. *Back cover:* blank. Olive green and white leaf-design endpapers.

"Copyright by Fairbanks, Palmer & Co., 1881," p. [4].

Contains black-and-white illustration signed "K.G.," p. 274, and unsigned black-and-white illustration by K.G., p. 145.

Copy imperfect, lacking pp. 49–112.

Presented by the Friends of the Detroit Public Library.

135. Miller, Nancy Minerva Haynes

MOTHER TRUTH'S | MELODIES. | COMMON SENSE FOR CHILDREN. | A KINDERGARTEN. | BY | MRS. E. P. MILLER, | AUTHOR OF "A FATHER'S ADVICE: A BOOK FOR EVERY BOY," AND "A MOTHER'S | ADVICE: A BOOK FOR EVERY GIRL." | NEARLY 400 ILLUSTRATIONS. | NEW AND EN- LARGED EDITION. | CHICAGO: | FAIRBANKS AND PALMER PUBLISHING CO. | 1885.

[ii] [7] 8–296 [ii] p. 18.3 cm.

"Copyright by Fairbanks, Palmer & Co., 1881," p. [4].

Contains unsigned black-and-white illustration by K.G., p. 145, and black-and-white illustration signed "K.G.," p. 274.

a. Red cloth. *Front cover:* same as item 134. *Spine:* same as item 134. *Back cover:* same as item 134. Olive green and white floral endpapers.

b. Red cloth. *Front cover:* same as item 134. *Spine:* same as item 134. *Back cover:* same as item 134. Olive green and white leaf-design endpapers.

136. Miller, Nancy Minerva Haynes

MOTHER TRUTH'S | MELODIES. | COMMON SENSE FOR CHILDREN. | A KINDERGARTEN, | BY | MRS. E. P. MILLER, | AUTHOR OF "A FATHER'S ADVICE: A BOOK FOR EVERY BOY," AND | "A MOTHER'S ADVICE: A BOOK FOR EVERY GIRL." | 450 ILLUSTRATIONS. | NEW AND ENLARGED EDI- TION. | CHICAGO: | FAIRBANKS & PALMER PUBLISHING CO. | NEW YORK: M. W. HAZEN CO. ATCHISON, KAS.: L. A. DAVIS & CO. | HARRISBURG: PENNSYLVANIA PUB- LISHING CO. | 1887

[ii] [7] 8–352 [ii] p. 18.3 cm.

Red cloth. *Front cover:* same as item 134. *Spine:* same as item 134. *Back cover:* same as item 134. All edges gilt. Olive green and white floral endpapers.

"Copyright by Fairbanks & Palmer Publishing Co. 1881 & 1887," p. [4].

Contains black-and-white illustrations signed "K.G.," p. 324, and unsigned black-and-white illustrations by K.G., pp. 157, 248, 255, 256, and 282.

Presented by the Friends of the Detroit Public Library.

137. MISS ROSEBUD | AND OTHER STORIES | PROFUSELY ILLUSTRATED | BOSTON | D LOTHROP COMPANY | WASHINGTON STREET OPPOSITE BROMFIELD

[32] p. 23.0 cm.

White glazed pictorial boards. *Front cover:* Miss Rosebud | ARMSTRONG & CO. LITH. BOSTON, printed in pink and blue; picture of two children playing with dolls and serving tea, in circular frame, printed in colors. *Spine:* blank. *Back cover:* two girls in winter attire walking on ice, printed in colors. Pages [1–2] and [31–32] used as pastedowns.

"Copyright, 1888, by D. Lothrop Company," p. [4].

"Miss Rose-Bud. (Engraved from the Original Painting by Kate Greenaway, owned by D. Lothrop & Co.)," p. [2], printed in black and white.

Presented by the Friends of the Detroit Public Library.

138. Mother Goose

MOTHER GOOSE | or the | OLD NURSERY RhYMES | Illustrated by | KATE GREENAWAY | engraved and | printed by | EDMUND EVANS | London and New York: | George Routledge and Sons. | [Copyright.]

[4] 5–48 p.

a. 17.1 cm.

Yellow glazed pictorial wrappers. *Front cover:* MOTHER GOOSE | Illustrated By | KATE GREENAWAY, printed in black; picture of young girl with bonnet and muff holding an umbrella in one hand and a bouquet of roses in the other hand, printed in colors; surrounded by a garland of ivy and a single line, printed in black with red shading. *Spine:* blank. *Back cover:* same as front cover. White endpapers.

Page number printed upside down, p. 38.

Presented by John S. Newberry.

b. 17.0 cm.

Pinkish beige cloth. *Front cover:* MOTHER GOOSE | ILLUS-TRATED | BY | KATE GREENAWAY., stamped in black; picture of young girl carrying a pail, and a sprig of flowers, stamped in gold and colors. *Spine:* blank. *Back cover:* blank. All edges stained red. White endpapers.

Presented by the Friends of the Detroit Public Library.

c. 16.8 cm.

White cloth. *Front cover:* MOTHER GOOSE, printed in brown; title surrounded by olive green latticework design. *Spine:* pink cloth. *Back cover:* same as front cover. All edges stained orange. Olive green endpapers.

Salmon-colored dust wrapper. *Front:* THREE SHILLINGS AND SIXPENCE. | MOTHER GOOSE | OR THE | Old Nursery Rhymes. | Illustrated by | KATE GREENAWAY. | Engraved and Printed by | EDMUND EVANS. | LONDON AND NEW YORK: GEORGE ROUTLEDGE & SONS, printed in red; picture of six children dancing in a circle, printed in red. *Spine:* blank. *Back:* blank.

"Contents of this book," verso of front endpaper.

"London Engraved & Printed at Racquet Court, by Edmund Evans," recto of back endpaper.

Contains the bookplate of Charles Plumptre Johnson.

From the collection of Robert Partridge.

Presented by the Friends of the Detroit Public Library.

d. 16.8 cm.

Yellow glazed pictorial boards. *Front cover:* same as item 138*a*. *Spine:* pink cloth. *Back cover:* same as item 138*a*. All edges stained pink. Olive green endpapers.

Salmon-colored dust wrapper; design same as item 138*c*.

"Contents of this book," verso of front flyleaf.

Page number printed upside down, p. 10.

"London Engraved & Printed at Racquet Court, by Edmund Evans," recto of back endpaper.

Presented by the Friends of the Detroit Public Library.

e. 16.8 cm.

Turquoise cloth. *Front cover:* MOTHER GOOSE | ILLUS-TRATED | BY | KATE GREENAWAY., stamped in black; picture of young girl carrying a pail, and a sprig of flowers, stamped in colors. *Spine:* blank. *Back cover:* publisher's monogram in center, stamped in black. Turquoise endpapers.

Page number printed upside down, p. 38.

Inscription dated "Xmas 1888," front flyleaf.

139. Mother Goose

MOTHER GOOSE | or the | OLD NURSERY RhYMES | Illus-trated by | KATE GREENAWAY | as originally | engraved and | printed by | EDMUND EVANS | New York: | George Routledge and Sons. | [Author's Edition.]

[4] 5–48 p. 17.2 cm.

"Contents of This Book," verso of front flyleaf.

"Drawn on Stone & Printed by Wemple & Company. Art Lithographers New York," recto of back flyleaf.

a. Pink glazed pictorial boards. *Front cover:* MOTHER GOOSE | KATE GREENAWAY., printed in brown; picture of mother and child and two young girls in winter attire, printed in colors. *Spine:* dark blue cloth. *Back cover:* same as front cover. All edges stained pink. Olive green endpapers.

Inscription dated "Christmas 1884," recto of front flyleaf.

Presented by John S. Newberry.

b. Pink glazed pictorial boards. *Front cover:* same as item 139*a.* *Spine:* same as item 139*a.* *Back cover:* same as item 139*a.* All edges stained red. Olive green endpapers.

Presented by the Friends of the Detroit Public Library.

140. Mother Goose

MOTHER GOOSE | or the | OLD NURSERY RhYMES | Illus-trated by | KATE GREENAWAY | LONDON | FREDERICK WARNE AND CO. | AND NEW YORK.

[1] 2–52 p. 15.8 cm.

Olive green suede, rounded corners. *Front cover:* Mother Goose | or | The Old Nursery | Rhymes | By | Kate Greenaway, stamped in gold; picture of several children holding hands in a circle, stamped in gold. *Spine:* blank. *Back cover:* blank. All edges gilt. White endpapers with flowers printed in colors within two-line olive green border.

"Copyright all rights reserved," verso front flyleaf.

"Engraved and printed by Edmund Evans Ltd. at the Racquet Court Press, London, S.E.," recto back flyleaf.

Presented by the Friends of the Detroit Public Library.

141. Mother Goose

MOTHER GOOSE | or the | OLD NURSERY RhYMES | Illus-trated by | KATE GREENAWAY | LONDON | FREDERICK

WARNE AND CO. LTD. | AND NEW YORK
Two sheets of forty-eight uncut pages.
"Printed in Great Britain," verso of title page.
From the collection of Robert Partridge.
Presented by the Friends of the Detroit Public Library.

142. Mother Goose
MOTHER GOOSE | or the | OLD NURSERY RhYMES | Illus-
trated by | KATE GREENAWAY | LONDON | FREDERICK
WARNE AND CO. LTD | AND NEW YORK
[1] 2–52 p. 16.2 cm.
a. Cream-colored glazed pictorial boards. *Front cover:*
MOTHER GOOSE | Illustrated by | KATE GREENAWAY | Little
maid, little maid, | Whither goest thou? | Down in the meadow |
To milk my cow., printed in black; picture of young maid with
milking pail enclosed within trellis border entwined with roses,
printed in colors. *Spine:* olive green cloth; MOTHER GOOSE,
stamped in black. *Back cover:* blank. White endpapers with flowers printed in colors within two-line olive green border.
"Copyright All Rights Reserved," verso front flyleaf.
"Engraved and printed by Edmund Evans, Ltd. Rose Place,
Globe Road, London, E.," recto of back flyleaf.
Presented by Mrs. Austin G. Melcher.

b. Cream-colored pictorial boards. *Front cover:* same as item
142*a*. *Spine:* dark green cloth. *Back cover:* blank. Endpapers: same
as item 142*a*.
Front flyleaf lacking.
"Printed in Great Britain 280.1140," p. [4].
"Engraved and Printed by Edmund Evans, Ltd. Rose Place,
Globe Road, London, E.," recto back flyleaf.
Accompanied by uncut sheet of sixteen pages including title
page. "Printed in Great Britain 583.247," verso of title page.
Presented by the Friends of the Detroit Public Library.

143. Mother Goose
MOTHER GOOSE | or the | OLD NURSERY RhYMES | after |
KATE GREENAWAY | McLOUGHLIN BRO'S, PUBLISHERS,
N. Y.
[48] p.
Rebound copy with original cover laid on. *Front cover:*
MOTHER | GOOSE | OR THE | OLD NURSERY | RHYMES |
WITH | ILLUSTRATIONS | AFTER | KATE GREENAWAY. |
NEW-YORK McLOUGHLIN BROTHERS, printed in black and
red; picture of young maid with milking pail and sprigs of flow-

ers, printed in colors. *Back cover:* MOTHER | GOOSE, printed in red; sprigs of flowers, printed in colors.

Since this copy has been rebound, it is not known whether any pages are missing or whether the original binding was wrappers or boards.

144. Mother Goose
SCÈNES FAMILIÈRES | PAR J. GIRARDIN | AVEC LES DESSINS | DE | KATE GREENAWAY | PARIS: LIBRAIRIE HACHETTE ET CIE | 79, BOULEVARD SAINT-GERMAIN, 79.
[4] 5–48 p. 16.2 cm.

Yellow glazed pictorial boards. *Front cover:* SCÈNES FAMILIÈRES | PARIS | LIBRAIRIE HACHETTE ET CIE, printed in black; same design as item 138*a. Spine:* Pink cloth. *Back cover:* same as front cover. All edges stained pink. Olive green endpapers.

"Gravé et imprimé par Edmund Evans, Racquet-ct., Fleet-st., Londres," p. [4], printed over dedication statement.

Page number printed upside down, p. 16.

"Gravé et Imprimé par Edmund Evans, Racquet Court, Fleet Street, Londres," recto back endpaper.

Presentation inscription dated "July 1890," recto front flyleaf.

Presented by the Friends of the Detroit Public Library.

145. Mulholland, Rosa
PUCK AND BLOSSOM | A Fairy Tale | BY | ROSA MULHOL-LAND | AUTHOR OF "THE LITTLE FLOWER-SEEKERS," "ELDER GOWAN," ETC. | WITH SIX ILLUSTRATIONS, IN GOLD AND COLORS | London: | MARCUS WARD & CO., 67 & 68, CHANDOS STREET, STRAND | AND ROYAL ULSTER WORKS, BELFAST
[9] 10–128 p. 20.5 cm.

Dark green cloth, beveled edges. *Front cover:* PUCK | AND | BLOSSOM | A FAIRY TALE, stamped in gold and black; decorative design, stamped in black; picture of flowers, printed in colors on glazed paper pasted on left-hand side of cover; triple-line border, stamped in black and gold. *Spine:* PUCK | AND | BLOSSOM | MARCUS | WARD | & CO., stamped in gold and black; decorative design, stamped in black and gold. *Back cover:* double-line border, blind-stamped. White endpapers.

"Marcus Ward & Co., Printers, Royal Ulster Works, Belfast," p. 128.

Presentation inscription dated "Xmas 1879," recto front flyleaf.

Contains six unsigned illustrations by K.G. printed in gold

and colors on stiff glazed paper and mounted within a black-and-white ornamental border, pp. [4, 31, 61, 79, 107, and 117].

Presented by the Friends of the Detroit Public Library.

146. Percy, Cotton F., and Frances Collins
MUDGE | AND HER CHICKS. | BY | A BROTHER AND SIS-TER. | NEW YORK: | E. P. DUTTON & CO., | 31 WEST 23RD STREET. | LONDON: GRIFFITH, FARRAN, OKEDEN & WELSH.

[6] 7–288 [3] 4–15 [16] p. 16.2 cm.

Blue cloth. *Front cover:* MUDGE, stamped in blue on gold rectangle; picture of two girls sitting on the bough of a tree reading a book, stamped in black and gold. *Spine:* MUDGE, stamped in blue on gold; trunk of tree, stamped in gold. *Back cover:* blank. White endpapers.

Copy imperfect, lacking pages [1–2] and 13–14.

"The rights of translation and of reproduction are reserved," p. [4].

"Morrison and Gibb, Edinburgh, Printers to her Majesty's Stationery Office. 3M—5/86—V.," p. 288.

"A Selection from E. P. Dutton and Company's Catalogue of New & Approved Books for the Home and the Sunday School. New York: E. P. Dutton & Co., 31, West Twenty-Third Street. London: Griffith, Farran, Okeden & Welsh. 40M-4.86—V.T. & S.," pp. [3] 4–15 [16] at end.

Publisher's device, p. [16] at end.

Contains black-and-white illustration signed "GREENAWAY, DEL.," p. 191, and black-and-white illustration signed "K. GREENAWAY, DEL.," p. 269.

147. LE PETIT LIVRE | des Souvenirs | TEXTE PAR MME COL-OMB | ILLUSTRATIONS DE KATE GREENAWAY | PARIS | LIBRAIRIE HACHETTE ET CIE | 79, BOULEVARD SAINT-GERMAIN, 79.

[4] 5–126 [127–30] p. (i.e., 266[?] p.) 9.0 cm.

Covers lacking. All edges stained yellow.

French edition of *Kate Greenaway's Birthday Book for Children.*

Page count uncertain since covers are lacking; some preliminary leaves may be missing.

148. Pollock, Walter Herries
AMATEUR THEATRICALS. | BY | WALTER HERRIES POL-LOCK | AND | LADY POLLOCK. | LONDON: | MACMILLAN AND CO. | 1879. | The Right of Translation and Reproduction is Reserved.

[vii] viii–[xii] [1] 2–71 [72] [4] p. 18.0 cm.

Light blue cloth. *Front cover:* ART AT HOME | AMATEUR | THEATRICALS | POLLOCK, stamped in black; publisher's monogram, stamped in black. *Spine:* AMATEUR THEATRI-CALS POLLOCK, stamped in black. *Back cover:* ART | AT | HOME | SERIES, stamped in black. Brown endpapers.

"London: R. Clay, Sons and Taylor, Bread Street Hill.," p. [72].

Advertisements for W. Clarkson, Macmillan and Co., and Dick Radclyffe & Co., pp. [1–4] at end.

Contains three black-and-white illustrations signed "K.G.," pp. [1] 17, and 54.

From the collection of Robert Partridge.

Presented by the Friends of the Detroit Public Library.

149. Potter, F. Scarlett

MELCOMB MANOR | A Family Chronicle | ARRANGED FROM THE PAPERS OF RICHARD BRENT, ESQ., | SOME-TIME OF MELCOMB | BY | F. SCARLETT POTTER | AUTHOR OF "THE VOLSUNG TALE," ETC. | WITH SIX ILLUS-TRATIONS, IN GOLD AND COLORS | London: | MARCUS WARD & CO., 67 & 68, CHANDOS STREET, COVENT GAR-DEN | NEW YORK: POTT, YOUNG, & CO., COOPER UNION, FOURTH AVENUE | 1875

[5] 6–148 p. 20.5 cm.

Terracotta cloth, beveled edges. *Front cover:* MELCOMB | MANOR | A FAMILY CHRONICLE, stamped in gold and black; picture of flowers printed in colors on glazed paper pasted on left-hand side of cover; decorative design, stamped in black; triple-line border, stamped in black and gold. *Spine:* MELCOMB | MANOR | MARCUS | WARD | & CO., stamped in black and gold; decorative design, stamped in black and gold. *Back cover:* trellis design with single-line border, blind-stamped. Dark blue endpapers.

"Marcus Ward & Co., Printers, Royal Ulster Works, Belfast," p. 148.

Contains six unsigned illustrations by K.G., printed in gold and colors on stiff paper and mounted on pp. [2, 49, 61, 89, 131, and 145] (illustration entitled "The Messenger," p. [2]; "News from Far," p. [145]).

Presented by the Friends of the Detroit Public Library.

150. Potter, F. Scarlett

MELCOMB MANOR | A Family Chronicle | ARRANGED FROM THE PAPERS OF RICHARD BRENT, ESQ., | SOME-

TIME OF MELCOMB | BY | F. SCARLETT POTTER | AUTHOR OF "THE VOLSUNG TALE," ETC. | WITH SIX ILLUS-TRATIONS, IN GOLD AND COLORS | London: | MARCUS WARD & CO., 67 & 68, CHANDOS STREET, COVENT GARDEN | AND ROYAL ULSTER WORKS, BELFAST

[5] 6–148 p.

"Marcus Ward & Co., Printers, Royal Ulster Works, Belfast," p. 148.

Contains six unsigned illustrations by K.G., printed in gold and colors on stiff paper and mounted on pp. [2, 49, 61, 89, 131, and 145].

a. 20.7 cm.

Blue cloth, beveled edges. *Front cover:* same as item 149. *Spine:* same as item 149. *Back cover:* same as item 149. Dark blue endpapers.

Presentation inscription dated "Christmas '75," p. [1].

Illustration entitled "The Messenger," p. [2]; "News from Far," p. [145].

From the collection of Robert Partridge.

Presented by the Friends of the Detroit Public Library.

b. 20.6 cm.

Blue cloth, beveled edges. *Front cover:* same as item 149 except that different flowers are printed in colors on glazed paper. *Spine:* same as item 149. *Back cover:* double-line border, blind-stamped.

Illustration entitled "News from Far," p. [2]; "The Messenger," p. [145].

Presented by the Friends of the Detroit Public Library.

151.   The Quiver of Love | A COLLECTION OF | VALENTINES | ANCIENT AND MODERN | With Illustrations in Colors | FROM DRAWINGS BY | WALTER CRANE AND K. GREENAWAY | London: | MARCUS WARD & CO., 67 & 68, CHANDOS STREET, STRAND | AND ROYAL ULSTER WORKS, BELFAST | 1876

[vi] [7] 8–152 p.

Added title page printed in gold and colors.

"Printed by Marcus Ward and Co., Royal Ulster Works Belfast," p. [2].

Contains eight unsigned illustrations, printed in gold and colors on stiff paper and mounted within printed borders, inserted as frontispiece to added title page and after pages 26, 32, 44, 60, 84, 114, and 138. Four of the illustrations are by K.G.

a. 21.8 cm.

Brown cloth, beveled edges. *Front cover:* THE | QUIVER OF LOVE, stamped in gold on white rectangle in center; cupids in each corner, top two holding banner with words "Amor Vincit Omnia," stamped in gold; decorative border, stamped in gold. *Spine:* THE | QUIVER | OF | LOVE | MARCUS WARD & CO., stamped in gold; two cupids, stamped in gold. *Back cover:* double-line border, blind-stamped. All edges gilt. Dark blue endpapers.

Presented by John S. Newberry.

b. 21.8 cm.

Brown cloth, beveled edges. *Front cover:* same as item 151*a* except that title is stamped in gold on turquoise rectangle in center. *Spine:* same as item 151*a*. *Back cover:* diagonal lattice design with double-line border, blind-stamped. All edges gilt. Dark blue endpapers.

Presented by the Friends of the Detroit Public Library.

c. 21.9 cm.

Green cloth, beveled edges. *Front cover:* same as item 151*a*. *Spine:* same as item 151*a*. *Back cover:* same as item 151*a*. All edges gilt. Pale yellow endpapers.

From the collection of Robert Partridge.

Presented by the Friends of the Detroit Public Library.

d. 21.6 cm.

Blue cloth, beveled edges. *Front cover:* same as item 151*a* except that title is stamped in gold on blue cloth. *Spine:* same as item 151*a*. *Back cover:* same as item 151*a*. All edges gilt. Brown endpapers.

Contains only six illustrations. No illustrations after pages 32 and 138. Three of the illustrations are by K.G.

Bookplate of Charles Plumtre Johnson.

From the collection of Robert Partridge.

Presented by the Friends of the Detroit Public Library.

152. Ranking, B. Montgomerie

FLOWERS & FANCIES | Valentines | ANCIENT AND MODERN | BY B. MONTGOMERIE RANKING | AND | THOMAS K. TULLY, F.R.H.S. | With Illustrations in Colour by | KATE GREENAWAY | London: | MARCUS WARD & CO., 67, CHANDOS STREET | AND ROYAL ULSTER WORKS, BEL-FAST | 1882

[5] 10–186 [187–88] p. 11.1 cm.

Brown cloth. *Front cover:* Flowers & Fancies | A | Collection | of | Valentine Verses | Illustrated by | Kate Greenaway, stamped in silver and black; picture of girl and boy reading a book enclosed in a circle, stamped in black; sprig of flowers and butterflies in upper left-hand corner, stamped in silver and black. *Spine:* Flowers | & | Fancies | Valentine | Verses, stamped in silver and black; sprigs of flowers, stamped in silver and black. *Back cover:* double-line border, blind-stamped. White endpapers.

"Marcus Ward & Co., Royal Ulster Works, Belfast," p. 186.

Contains four inserted illustrations.

Presented by the Friends of the Detroit Public Library.

153. Ranking, B. Montgomerie

FLOWERS & FANCIES | Valentines | ANCIENT AND MODERN | BY B. MONTGOMERIE RANKING | AND | THOMAS K. TULLY, F.R.H.S. | With Illustrations in Colour by | KATE GREENAWAY | London: | MARCUS WARD & CO., 67, CHANDOS STREET | AND AT BELFAST AND NEW YORK | 1883

[5?] 10–186 [187–88?] p. 11.2 cm.

Rebound in dark blue calf. Original front cover used as front pastedown; green cloth; same design as item 152, stamped in black and silver. All edges gilt.

"Marcus Ward & Co., Royal Ulster Works, Belfast," p. 186.

Presented by the Friends of the Detroit Public Library.

154. Ranking, B. Montgomerie

The Quiver of Love | A COLLECTION OF | VALENTINES | ANCIENT & MODERN | BY B. MONTGOMERIE RANKING | AND | THOMAS K. TULLY, F.R.H.S. | With Illustrations in Colour | London: | MARCUS WARD & CO., 67, CHANDOS STREET | AND ROYAL ULSTER WORKS, BELFAST | 1880

[9] 10–186 [6] p. 14.8 cm.

Brown cloth. *Front cover:* THE | QUIVER OF LOVE, stamped in gold; cupids in each corner, stamped in gold; top two cupids holding banner with words "Amor Vincit Omnia," and triple-line border, stamped in gold. *Spine:* THE | QUIVER | OF | LOVE | MARCUS WARD & CO., stamped in gold; cupids above and below title, stamped in gold. *Back cover:* double-line border, blind-stamped. All edges gilt. Brown endpapers.

Frontispiece and added title page inserted after p. [4].

"Marcus Ward & Co., Royal Ulster Works, Belfast," p. 186.

"A Selected List From Messrs. Marcus Ward & Co.'s Publications," pp. [1–6] at end.

Contains four unsigned illustrations by K.G., printed in gold and colors, inserted after pp. 48, 80, 112, and 160.

Presented by the Friends of the Detroit Public Library.

155. Richards, Laura E.

FIVE MICE IN A MOUSE-TRAP, | BY THE | MAN IN THE MOON. | DONE IN VERNACULAR, | FROM THE LUNACU-LAR, | BY LAURA E. RICHARDS, | Author of "Babyhood," Etc. | WITH ILLUSTRATIONS BY | KATE GREENAWAY, ADDIE LEDYARD, AND OTHERS. | BOSTON: | PUBLISHED BY ESTES AND LAURIAT, | 299 TO 305 WASHINGTON STREET, | 1880.

[vii] viii 9–228 [229–30] p.

"Copyright by Estes & Lauriat, 1880," p. [vi].

Contains black-and-white illustrations signed "K.G.," pp. 21, 72, 80, 103, 123, 124, 126, 137, 155, 156, 160, 183, 200, 208, 209, and 212, and unsigned black-and-white illustrations by K.G., pp. 79, 154, and 182.

a. 21.1 cm.

Pictorial boards. *Front cover:* Five Little | Mice | in a | Mouse | Trap | By the | Man in the Moon. | BOSTON | ESTES | & | LAURIAT., printed in black; pictures of five mice in a mousetrap and an old man and his dog, printed in colors; single-line border, printed in black. *Spine:* Five Little Mice, printed in black on a sign being held by five mice. *Back cover:* one mouse in each corner and one in the center, printed in colors; single-line border, printed in black. Endpapers contain illustrations by K.G., printed in various shades of blue.

Inscription dated "Xmas /80," p. [i].

Presented by the Friends of the Detroit Public Library.

b. 21.0 cm.

Blue cloth, beveled edges. *Front cover:* same as item 155*a*, stamped in black and gold. *Spine:* same as item 155*a*, stamped in black and gold. *Back cover:* same as item 155*a*, stamped in black and gold. Endpapers contain illustrations by K.G., printed in various shades of blue.

Presented by the Friends of the Detroit Public Library.

156. Richards, Laura E.

FIVE MICE IN A MOUSE-TRAP, | BY THE | MAN IN THE MOON. | DONE IN VERNACULAR, | FROM THE LUNACU-LAR, | BY LAURA E. RICHARDS, | Author of "Babyhood," Etc. | WITH ILLUSTRATIONS BY | KATE GREENAWAY, ADDIE LEDYARD, AND OTHERS. | BOSTON: | PUBLISHED BY

ESTES AND LAURIAT, | 299 TO 305 WASHINGTON STREET, | [v] x [11] 12–228 p. (i.e., 224 p.) 20.9 cm.

Pictorial boards. *Front cover:* FIVE LITTLE MICE in | A MOUSE | TRAP | BY THE MAN IN THE MOON | ESTES & LAURIAT, printed in brown; picture of a cupid and an owl sitting on a tree limb with a clock suspended from it, being watched by five mice, printed in colors; girl and boy watching mice, printed in colors. *Spine:* FIVE | LITTLE | MICE | E & L | BOSTON, printed in brown; five mice, printed in white. *Back cover:* FIVE LITTLE MICE IN A MOUSE TRAP | BY THE | MAN | IN THE MOON | Armstrong & Co. Lith. Boston, printed in brown; decorative design of flowers and five mice, printed in colors. Endpapers contain illustrations by K.G., printed in various shades of blue.

"Copyright, by Estes & Lauriat, 1880," p. [4].

Contains black-and-white illustrations signed "K.G.," pp. 21, 72, 80, 103, 123, 124, 126, 137, 155, 156, 160, 183, 200, 208, 209, and 212, and unsigned black-and-white illustrations by K.G., pp. 79, 154, and 182.

157.* Routledge, George, & Sons
CHRISTMAS, 1881. | GEORGE ROUTLEDGE & SONS' | COLOURED CATALOGUE OF | NEW CHRISTMAS BOOKS. | Illustration from "Kate Greenaway's Birthday Book | for Children." 2s. 6d.

[1] 2–[16] p., including covers. 10.3 cm.

Pictorial wrappers. *Front cover:* title taken from cover printed in red and black; illustration signed "K.G.," of small girl and boy holding hands, printed in colors; single-line border, printed in red. *Back cover:* Illustration from "Some of My Little Friends." by Mrs. Sale Barker. | With 24 full page Plates, printed in Colours by Kronheim & Co. | Boards. 2s. 6d.: cloth. 3s. 6d., printed in black; picture of girl on a swing, printed in colors; single-line border, printed in red.

"George Routledge & Sons' List of New Christmas Books," p. 2.

Contains colored illustrations by K.G., pp. [4, 5, and 13].

From the collection of Robert Partridge.

Presented by the Friends of the Detroit Public Library.

158. Ruskin, John
DAME WIGGINS OF LEE, | AND HER | SEVEN WONDERFUL CATS: | A HUMOROUS TALE | WRITTEN PRINCIPALLY

*Illustrated.

98

157. Paper cover.

160. *Fors Clavigera, 1884.*

BY A LADY OF NINETY. | EDITED, WITH ADDITIONAL
VERSES, | BY JOHN RUSKIN, LL.D., | HONORARY STUDENT
OF CHRIST CHURCH, | AND HONORARY FELLOW OF
CORPUS CHRISTI COLLEGE, OXFORD. | AND WITH NEW
ILLUSTRATIONS | BY KATE GREENAWAY. | WITH
TWENTY-TWO WOODCUTS. | GEORGE ALLEN, | SUN-
NYSIDE, ORPINGTON, KENT. | 1885.

"Printed by Hazell, Watson, and Viney, Ld., London and
Aylesbury.," p. [ii].

Printing and most of the page numbers on inner forms only;
outer forms blank.

a. [ix] 1–20 [21] p. (i.e., 48 p.) 18.5 cm.

Dark green cloth. *Front cover:* DAME WIGGINS OF LEE.,
stamped in gold; picture of cat painting a portrait, stamped in
gold; single-line border, blind-stamped. *Spine:* blank. *Back cover:*
single-line border, blind-stamped. All edges speckled red.
White endpapers.

Presented by John S. Newberry.

b. [ix] 1–20 [21] p. (i.e., 48 p.) 18.5 cm.

Gray cloth. *Front cover:* same as item 158*a*. *Spine:* same as item
158*a*. *Back cover:* same as item 158*a*. All edges speckled red.
White endpapers.

From the collection of Robert Partridge.

Presented by the Friends of the Detroit Public Library.

c. [ix] 1–20 [21] p. (i.e., 48 p.) 18.5 cm.

Brown cloth. *Front cover:* same as item 158*a*. *Spine:* same as
item 158*a*. *Back cover:* same as item 158*a*. All edges speckled red.
White endpapers.

Inscribed presentation: "Maud Locker Lampson From Kate
Greenaway 1886.," recto front endpaper.

Presented by John S. Newberry.

d. [2] [iii] iv [v–ix] 1–20 [21–24] p. (i.e., 52 p.) 21.8 cm.

Gray cloth. *Front cover:* same as item 158*a*. *Spine:* same as item
158*a*. *Back cover:* same as item 158*a*. All edges uncut. Gray and
white endpapers with fleur-de-lis design.

Presented by John S. Newberry.

159. Ruskin, John

FORS CLAVIGERA. | LETTERS | TO THE WORKMEN AND
LABOURERS | OF GREAT BRITAIN. | BY | JOHN RUSKIN,
LL.D., | HONORARY STUDENT OF CHRIST CHURCH, AND
SLADE PROFESSOR OF FINE ART. | VOL. VIII. | GEORGE

ALLEN, | SUNNYSIDE, ORPINGTON, KENT. | 1878-80-83-84.

[iv] 1–306 p. 22.6 cm.

Light blue boards. *Front cover:* blank. *Spine:* RUSKIN | FORS | CLAVIGERA. | VOL. VIII., printed in black on paper label. *Back cover:* blank. White endpapers.

Contains black-and-white illustrations by K.G., pp. [179, 215, 231, 250, and 251].

Presented by the Friends of the Detroit Public Library.

160.* Ruskin, John

FORS CLAVIGERA. | LETTERS | TO THE WORKMEN AND LABOURERS | OF GREAT BRITAIN. | BY JOHN RUSKIN, LL.D. | LETTER THE 95th. | (ELEVENTH OF NEW SERIES.) | OCTOBER, 1884. | FORS INFANTIAE. | GEORGE ALLEN, | SUNNYSIDE, ORPINGTON, KENT.

[iv] [251] 252–81 [282–84] p. 22.4 cm.

Tan wrappers. *Front cover:* FORS CLAVIGERA. | LETTERS | TO THE WORKMEN AND LABOURERS | OF GREAT BRIT-AIN. | BY JOHN RUSKIN, LL.D. | LETTER THE 95th. | (ELEVENTH OF NEW SERIES.) | OCTOBER, 1884. | FORS IN-FANTIAE. | GEORGE ALLEN, | SUNNYSIDE, ORPINGTON, KENT. | Price Tenpence., printed in black; floral bouquet just below center, printed in black. *Spine:* blank. *Back cover:* ''***For reasons which will be explained in the course of these Letters, I wish to retain complete command over their mode of publica-tion. . . .''

Contains brown-and-white illustration signed ''K.G.,'' p. [251].

Presented by John S. Newberry.

161. Russell, Mary Annette Beauchamp

The | April Baby's Book of Tunes | WITH | THE STORY OF HOW THEY CAME | TO BE WRITTEN | BY THE AUTHOR OF | 'ELIZABETH AND HER GERMAN GARDEN' | ILLUSTRATED BY KATE GREENAWAY | London | MACMILLAN AND CO., LIMITED | NEW YORK: THE MACMILLAN COMPANY | 1900 | All rights reserved

[vii] 1–74 [75–76] p. Oblong. 18.9 x 19.6 cm.

Tan cloth. *Front cover:* The April Baby's | Book of Tunes | By the Author of | 'Elizabeth and her German Garden,' stamped in red and black; picture of young girl in winter attire carrying a pair of skates, stamped in colors. *Spine:* The April Baby's Book of

*Illustrated.

Tunes, stamped in black and red. *Back cover:* blank. All edges stained red. White endpapers.

"Copyright in the United States of America," p. [vi].

"Printed by R. & R. Clark, Limited, Edinburgh," p. [75].

Contains sixteen inserted illustrations.

Presented by John S. Newberry.

162. Russell, Mary Annette Beauchamp

The | April Baby's Book of Tunes | WITH | THE STORY OF HOW THEY CAME | TO BE WRITTEN | BY THE AUTHOR OF | "ELIZABETH AND HER GERMAN GARDEN" | ILLUS- TRATED BY KATE GREENAWAY | New York | THE MACMIL- LAN COMPANY | LONDON: MACMILLAN & CO., LTD. | 1900 | All rights reserved

[vi] 1–74 [75–76] [2] p. Oblong. 17.0 x 17.2 cm.

Tan cloth. *Front cover:* same as item 161. *Spine:* same as item 161. *Back cover:* blank. White endpapers.

"Copyright, 1900, by The Macmillan Company. Set up and electrotyped November, 1900. Reprinted November, 1900. Norwood Press J. S. Cushing & Co.—Berwick & Smith Nor- wood, Mass., U.S.A.," p. [iv].

Advertisements for *Elizabeth and her German Garden* and *The Solitary Summer,* pp. [1–2] at end.

Contains sixteen inserted illustrations.

Presented by the Friends of the Detroit Public Library.

163. Russell, Mary Annette Beauchamp

The | April Baby's Book of Tunes | WITH | THE STORY OF HOW THEY CAME | TO BE WRITTEN | BY THE AUTHOR OF | "ELIZABETH AND HER GERMAN GARDEN" | ILLUS- TRATED BY KATE GREENAWAY | New York | THE MAC- MILLAN COMPANY | LONDON: MACMILLAN & CO., LTD. | 1901 | All rights reserved

[vi] 1–74 [75–76] [2] p. 17.3 x 17.3 cm.

Light tan cloth. *Front cover:* same as item 161. *Spine:* same as item 161. *Back cover:* blank. White endpapers.

"Copyright, 1900, by The Macmillan Company. Set up and electrotyped November, 1900. Reprinted November, 1900; January, 1901. Norwood Press J. S. Cushing & Co.—Berwick & Smith Norwood, Mass., U.S.A.," p. [iv].

Advertisements for *Elizabeth and her German Garden* and *The Solitary Summer,* pp. [1–2] at end.

Contains sixteen inserted illustrations.

164. Sawtelle, Mrs. E. W.

THE BEST ORNAMENT. | BY | TRACY TOWNE, | AUTHOR OF "PET'S CHRISTMAS HONOR," "THE | BEST WAY," ETC. | BOSTON: | D. LOTHROP & CO., PUBLISHE'RS (*sic*), | FRANKLIN AND HAWLEY STREETS.

[116] p. 19.5 cm.

Glazed pictorial boards. *Front cover:* THE BEST ORNAMENT | BOSTON | D. LOTHROP | & CO. | PUBLISHERS | FARBES CO BOSTON, printed in red and black; cover divided diagonally with picture of girl reading a book in top half and a crown on a book surrounded by holly and leaves in bottom half, printed in colors. *Spine:* green cloth. *Back cover:* advertisement for *Wide Awake: The New Monthly Magazine for Young People of All Ages,* printed in blue. Cream-colored endpapers.

"Copyright by D. Lothrop & Co." and "Wright & Potter Printing Company, 79 Milk Street, Boston," p. [4].

Presentation inscription dated "Delaware, 1879," recto front flyleaf.

Contains one unsigned black-and-white illustration by K.G., p. [43].

Presented by F. L. Scharlach.

165. Selous, Henry Courtney

THE | CHILDREN OF THE PARSONAGE | BY THE AUTHOR OF | "GERTY AND MAY," "OUR WHITE VIOLET," | "SUNNY DAYS," "GRANNY'S STORY BOX," "NEW BABY," | ETC., ETC. | WITH ILLUSTRATIONS BY K. GREENAWAY | Second Edition | LONDON | GRIFFITH AND FARRAN | SUCCESSORS TO NEWBERY AND HARRIS | CORNER OF ST. PAUL'S CHURCHYARD | MDCCCLXXV. | (All rights reserved.)

[vii] viii [1] 2–136 [4] 5–32 p. 16.8 cm.

Light brown cloth. *Front cover:* THE | CHILDREN OF THE | PARSONAGE | BY THE AUTHOR OF "GERTY & MAY," stamped in gold and black; geometric design, stamped in black. *Spine:* The | CHILDREN | of the | PARSONAGE | GRIFFITH | & FARRAN, stamped in gold and black; geometric design, stamped in black. *Spine:* decorative border design, blind-stamped. Cream-colored endpapers.

"Watson and Hazell, Printers, London and Aylesbury.," p. 136.

"Original Juvenile Library. A Catalogue of New and Popular Works, principally for the Young. In Elegant Cloth Bindings. Suitable for Presents and School Prizes. Published by Griffith and Farran, (successors to Newbery and Harris), West Corner of St. Paul's Churchyard, London.," pp. [1]–32 at end.

Contains four inserted illustrations.

Presented by the Friends of the Detroit Public Library.

166.* Selous, Henry Courtney

THE | CHILDREN OF THE PARSONAGE. | BY THE AU-
THOR OF | "GERTY AND MAY," "OUR WHITE VIOLET,"
"SUNNY DAYS," "GRANNY'S STORY BOX," | "NEW
BABY," ETC., ETC. | WITH ILLUSTRATIONS BY K.
GREENAWAY | GRIFFITH & FARRAN | (SUCCESSORS TO
NEWBERY AND HARRIS) | WEST CORNER ST. PAUL'S
CHURCHYARD, LONDON | E. P. DUTTON & CO., NEW
YORK

[9] 10–159 [160] [3] 4–16 p. 16.0 cm.

Brown cloth. *Front cover:* CHILDREN OF THE PARSONAGE,
enclosed in a rectangular sign hanging from a tree, sign
stamped in gold; picture of young boy reading to two girls
under a tree, stamped in black and green. *Spine:* CHILDREN |
OF THE | PARSONAGE, stamped in gold, and DUTTON | &
CO., in rectangle at bottom, stamped in gold; leaves, stamped
in black and green. *Back cover:* double-line border, blind-
stamped. Yellow endpapers.

"(All rights reserved.)," p. [6].

"Turnbull & Spears, Printers. 3M—G.C.—4—83.," p. 159.

"A Selection From E. P. Dutton and Company's Catalogue of
New & Approved Books for the Home and the Sunday School.
New York: E. P. Dutton & Co., 39, West Twenty-Third Street.
London: Griffith and Farran, St. Paul's Churchyard. 50 M
3.84.," pp. [1]–16 at end.

Presented by Jess Toth.

167.   Stories Witty and Pictures Pretty | A FASCINATING BOOK
FOR CHILDREN | Copyright, 1896, by W. B. Conkey Company |
NEW YORK CHICAGO | W. B. CONKEY COMPANY, Pub-
lishers.

[60] p. 24.7 cm.

Glazed pictorial boards. *Front cover:* STORIES WITTY | AND |
PICTURES PRETTY | W. B. CONKEY COMPANY | NEW
YORK-CHICAGO, printed in red and gold; picture of child in
winter attire pulling a dog on a sled, printed in colors. *Spine:* red
cloth. *Back cover:* two girls petting a fawn, printed in colors.
White endpapers.

Presentation inscription dated "Dec. 25 1896," p. [1].

Contains black-and-white illustrations signed "K.G.," pp.

*Illustrated.

166. Frontispiece, *The Children of the Parsonage.*

171. Title page.

[36] and [59], and unsigned black-and-white illustrations by K.G., pp. [38, 54, 55, and 58].

Presented by Mrs. George E. Schott in memory of George E. Barrett.

168. Taylor, Jane, and Ann Taylor
LITTLE ANN | AND | OTHER POEMS | BY | JANE AND ANN TAYLOR | ILLUSTRATED BY | KATE GREENAWAY | PRINTED IN COLOURS BY EDMUND EVANS | LONDON: GEORGE ROUTLEDGE & SONS | BROADWAY, LUDGATE HILL | NEW YORK: 9, LAFAYETTE PLACE | [The Illustrations are Copyright.]
[7] 8–64 p. 22.9 cm.
Cream-colored glazed pictorial boards, with olive green cloth corners. *Front cover:* LITTLE ANN | A BOOK | ILLUSTRATED BY | KATE GREENAWAY | Printed in Colours By | Edmund Evans, printed in pink and brown; two rows of seated children each holding a letter of the title, printed in colors. *Spine:* olive green cloth. *Back cover:* same as front cover. All edges stained blue. Bright yellow endpapers.
a. White dust jacket, with same design as front cover, printed in brown.
Presented by John S. Newberry.

b. Contains the bookplates of E. H. Mills and Frederick Locker. The Frederick Locker bookplate was designed by Kate Greenaway.
Presented by John S. Newberry.

c. Inscription dated "Xmas 1883," verso of front cover.
Presented by John S. Newberry.

169. Taylor, Jane, and Ann Taylor
LITTLE ANN | AND | OTHER PEOMS | BY | JANE AND ANN TAYLOR | LONDON | FREDERICK WARNE AND CO. | AND NEW YORK
[7] 8–64 p. 22.9 cm.
Cream-colored glazed pictorial boards, with olive green cloth corners. *Front cover:* LITTLE ANN | A BOOK | ILLUSTRATED BY | KATE GREENAWAY, printed in brown and pink; same design as item 168. *Spine:* olive green cloth; LITTLE ANN, stamped in black. *Back cover:* same as front cover. All edges stained yellow. Dark green endpapers.
Presented by the Friends of the Detroit Public Library.

170. Taylor, Jane, and Ann Taylor
POÈMES ENFANTINS | PAR | JANE ET ANN TAYLOR | ILLUSTRATIONS | DE | KATE GREENAWAY | TRADUCTION LIBRE | DE | J. GIRARDIN | PARIS | LIBRAIRIE HACHETTE ET CIE | 79, BOULEVARD SAINT-GERMAIN, 79 | 1883

[7] 8–64 p. 22.9 cm.

Cream-colored glazed pictorial boards, with olive green corners. *Front cover:* POÈMES ENFANTINS | PAR | JANE ET ANN TAYLOR | ILLUSTRATIONS | DE | KATE GREENAWAY | TRADUCTION LIBRE | DE | J. GIRARDIN, printed in pink and brown; two rows of children holding two signs, one containing the title, the other the author, printed in colors. *Spine:* olive green cloth. *Back cover:* same as front cover. All edges stained blue. Bright yellow endpapers.

French edition of *Little Ann.*

Presented by John S. Newberry.

171.* TOY LAND, | TROT'S JOURNEY, | AND | OTHER POEMS AND STORIES. | ILLUSTRATED | BY | KATE GREENAWAY. | NEW YORK: | R. WORTHINGTON, | 770 BROADWAY.

[2] 3–88 p. 24.0 cm.

Blue glazed pictorial boards. *Front cover:* TOY LAND | ILLUSTRATED by | KATE GREENAWAY. | NEW YORK. R WORTHINGTON., printed in white, gold, and red; picture of two small girls holding dolls, seated on high-legged chairs, apparently in a toy shop, printed in colors. *Spine:* blue cloth. *Back cover:* advertisement for "R. Worthington's New Juveniles for the Season of 1883–4." White endpapers.

"Copyright 1882, by R. Worthington" and "Press of J. J. Little & Co., Nos. 10 to 20 Astor Place, New York," p. [2].

Presented by the Friends of the Detroit Public Library.

172. Tupper, Margaret Elenora
LITTLE LOVING-HEART'S | POEM-BOOK. | BY | MARGARET ELENORA TUPPER. | WITH FORTY ILLUSTRATIONS. | NEW YORK: | E. P. DUTTON AND CO., | 713, BROADWAY. | GRIFFITH AND FARRAN, ST. PAUL'S CHURCHYARD, LONDON. | MDCCCLXXXII.

[vii] viii–xii [1] 2–164 [1] 2–16 p. 24.7 cm.

Blue and brown cloth. *Front cover:* LITTLE LOVING-HEART'S | POEM-BOOK | MARGARET ELENORA TUPPER, stamped in gold; unsigned illustrations by K.G. of boy with a horn and boy and girl holding hands, stamped in gold; floral

*Illustrated.

107

design stamped in black; cover diagonally divided with top half in blue cloth and bottom half in brown cloth. *Spine:* brown cloth: LITTLE | LOVING- | HEART'S | POEM- | BOOK | M. E. | TUP-PER | D&CO., stamped in gold; picture of girl and floral design, stamped in black and gold. *Back cover:* brown cloth; D&Co, blind-stamped in center. Gray and white floral endpapers.

"The rights of Translation and of Reproduction are reserved," p. [vi].

"Printed by Gilbert and Rivington, Limited, St. John's Square, London," p. 164.

"A Catalogue of New and Standard Works, Devotional and Religious Books, and Educational Literature, published by Griffith & Farran, West Corner of St. Paul's Churchyard, London. E. P. Dutton and Co., New York," pp. [1]–16 at end.

Inscription dated "Christmas 1882," p. [i].

Contains black-and-white illustrations signed "K.G.," pp. [36, 50, 55, 59, 77, 92, 110, and 118], and unsigned black-and-white illustrations by K.G., pp. [v] 6 [30] and [113].

Presented by "Miss Curtis."

173. Warne, Frederick, and Company
[BIRTHDAY BOOKS]
6 v.

In publisher's flip-top box. Dark red paper; floral design, printed in gold.

Presented by the Friends of the Detroit Public Library.

[v. 1] PRECEPT AND PROMISE | A | BIRTHDAY BOOK | [Quotation] | LONDON | FREDERICK WARNE & CO. | AND NEW YORK

[4] 5–157 [158] [2] p. 10.9 cm.

Salmon cloth. *Front cover:* Precept | & Promise | A Birthday | Book, stamped in gold; fourteen vertical lines, intertwined with ivy, stamped in dark brown; floral design, top and bottom, stamped in gold. *Spine:* Precept and Promise, stamped in dark brown; floral design from front cover continued at top and bottom, stamped in gold. *Back cover:* publisher's monogram in center and same design as front cover, stamped in dark brown. All edges stained salmon. Gray and white floral endpapers.

"Printed by Morrison & Gibb Limited, Edinburgh.," p. [4].

"List of Warne's Birthday Books," pp. [1–2] at end.

Contains colored frontispiece signed "K.G.," inserted after p. [2].

[v. 2] THE | QUOTATION | BIRTHDAY BOOK | [Quotation] | LONDON | FREDERICK WARNE & CO. | AND NEW YORK

[4] 5–157 [158] [2] p. 10.9 cm.

Green cloth. *Front cover:* The | Quotation | Birthday | Book, stamped in gold; with same vertical design as v. 1, stamped in dark green; same border design as v. 1, stamped in gold. *Spine:* The Quotation Birthday Book, stamped in dark green; same border design as v. 1, stamped in gold. *Back cover:* same as v. 1, stamped in dark green. All edges stained yellow. Gray and white floral endpapers.

"Printed by Morrison & Gibb Limited, Edinburgh.," p. [4].

"List of Warne's Birthday Books," pp. [1–2] at end.

Contains colored frontispiece signed "K.G.," inserted after p. [2].

[v. 3] GOLDEN LINKS; | A BIRTHDAY TEXT-BOOK. | BY | W. A. L. | [Quotation] | LONDON: | FREDERICK WARNE & CO. | AND NEW YORK.

[4] 5–156 [157–60] p. 10.9 cm.

White cloth. *Front cover:* Golden | Links | A Birthday | Book, stamped in gold; same vertical design as v. 1, stamped in olive green; same border design as v. 1, stamped in gold. *Spine:* Golden Links, stamped in olive green; same border design as v. 1, stamped in gold. *Back cover:* same as v. 1, stamped in olive green. All edges stained yellow. Gray and white floral endpapers.

Contains colored frontispiece signed "K.G.," inserted after p. [2].

[v. 4] SACRED GEMS: | A BIRTHDAY TEXT-BOOK, | WITH | DIARY FOR MEMORANDA. | BY | L. V. | [Quotation] | LONDON: | FREDERICK WARNE & CO. | AND NEW YORK.

[4] 5–156 [157–60] p. 10.9 cm.

Purple cloth. *Front cover:* Sacred | Gems | A Birthday | Book, stamped in gold; same vertical design as v. 1, stamped in dark purple; same border design as v. 1, stamped in gold. *Spine:* Sacred Gems, stamped in dark purple; same border design as v. 1, stamped in gold. *Back cover:* same as v. 1, stamped in dark purple. All edges stained orange. Light brown and white floral endpapers.

Contains colored frontispiece signed "K.G.," inserted after p. [2].

[v. 5] THE | Daily Motto Book. | A BIRTHDAY CALENDAR, | BY | L. V. | [Quotation] | LONDON: | FREDERICK WARNE & CO. | AND NEW YORK.

[4] 5–156 [157–60] p. 10.9 cm.

Light blue cloth. *Front cover:* The Daily | Motto | Book | A Birthday | Calendar, stamped in gold; same vertical design as v. 1, stamped in dark blue; same border design as v. 1, stamped in gold. *Spine:* The Daily Motto Book, stamped in dark blue; same border design as v. 1, stamped in gold. *Back cover:* same as v. 1, stamped in dark blue. All edges stained orange. Gray and white floral endpapers.

Contains unsigned colored frontispiece by K.G., inserted after p. [2].

[v. 6] THE BIRTHDAY BOOK | OF | PROVERBS | AND | MAXIMS | [Quotation] | LONDON | FREDERICK WARNE & CO. | AND NEW YORK

[4] 5–157 [158] [2] p. 10.9 cm.

Violet cloth. *Front cover:* The | Birthday Book | of | Proverbs | & Maxims, stamped in gold; same vertical design as v. 1, stamped in dark violet; same border design as v. 1, stamped in gold. *Spine:* Proverbs and Maxims, stamped in dark violet; same border design as v. 1, stamped in gold. *Back cover:* same as v. 1, stamped in dark violet. All edges stained salmon. Gray and white floral endpapers.

"Printed by Morrison & Gibb Limited, Edinburgh.," p. [4].

"List of Warne's Birthday Books," pp. [1–2] at end.

Contains unsigned colored frontispiece by K.G., inserted after p. [2].

174. Weatherly, Frederick Edward

THE ILLUSTRATED | Children's | BIRTHDAY-BOOK | EDITED, AND IN PART WRITTEN | BY | F. E. WEATHERLY. | With Illustrations by | KATE CRAUFORD, KATE GREEN-AWAY, ROBERT BARNES, | MRS. STAPLES, MISS BENNETT, MISS THOMAS, &C. | London: | W. MACK, 4, PATERNOSTER SQUARE.

"The engravings are by Messrs. W. & F. R. Cheshire," p. 286.

"J. Wright & Co. Printers, Bristol," p. 288.

Contains black-and-white illustrations signed "K.G.," pp. 76, 178, 202, 208, and 228, and unsigned black-and-white illustrations by K.G., pp. 24, 72, and 234.

a. [ii] [2] 3–288 p. 11.5 cm.

Pink cloth. *Front cover:* Children's BIRTHDAY BOOK | IL-LUSTRATED, stamped in red; picture of girl holding a hat and leaning against a fence, in a rectangular frame, stamped in red and brown; frame surrounded by floral design, stamped in brown. *Spine:* CHILDREN'S | BIRTHDAY | BOOK | W MACK, stamped in red; floral design, stamped in brown. *Back cover:* picture of girl in long dress holding a bouquet, stamped in red; double-line border, stamped in brown and red. Gray and white floral endpapers.

Presented by the Friends of the Detroit Public Library.

b. [ii] [4] 5–288 p. 11.6 cm.

Ivory glazed boards. *Front cover:* THE | CHILDRENS | BIRTH-DAY | BOOK, printed in gold and purple; purple and white flowers, surrounded by single-line border printed in gold. *Spine:* white imitation morocco; THE | ILLUSTRATED | Children's | BIRTHDAY | BOOK., stamped in gold. *Back cover:* sprig of flowers, printed in brown; wide single-line border enclosing narrow double-line border, printed in silver. All edges gilt. Gray floral endpapers.

Presented by the Friends of the Detroit Public Library.

175. Weatherly, Frederick Edward

THE ILLUSTRATED | Children's | BIRTHDAY-BOOK | EDITED, AND IN PART WRITTEN | BY | F. E. WEATHERLY. | With Illustrations by | KATE COLEMAN, KATE GREENAWAY, ROBERT BARNES, | MRS. STAPLES, MISS BENNETT AND OTHERS. | London: | W. MACK, 4, PATERNOSTER SQUARE.

[ii] [1] 2–286 [2] p.

Advertisement for *Dresden China and Other Songs* by F. E. Weatherly, pp. [1–2] at end.

Contains black-and-white illustrations signed "K.G.," pp. 76, 178, 202, 208, and 228, and unsigned black-and-white illustrations by K.G., pp. 24, 72, and 234.

a. 11.6 cm.

Light green cloth. *Front cover:* Children's | BIRTHDAY BOOK | ILLUSTRATED, stamped in red; picture of three children in rectangular frame, stamped in red; frame surrounded by floral design, stamped in brown. *Spine:* CHILDREN'S | BIRTHDAY | BOOK | W MACK, stamped in red; floral design, stamped in brown. *Back cover:* head of young child in circular frame, stamped in red and brown; double-line border, stamped in red and brown. Green and white floral endpapers.

Dot on each side of "Children's," title page.

Presentation inscription dated "April 20th, 1882," verso front flyleaf.

Presented by the Friends of the Detroit Public Library.

b. 11.4 cm.

Dark blue calf. *Front cover:* Children's | BIRTHDAY-BOOK, stamped in gold; picture of young man bowing to a seated woman, stamped in gold on a rectangular maroon morocco onlay; double-line border, blind-stamped. *Spine:* Birthday | Book, stamped in gold. *Back cover:* double-line border, blind-stamped. All edges gilt. Gray and white floral endpapers.

Presented by the Friends of the Detroit Public Library.

c. 11.6 cm.

Red morocco. *Front cover:* Children's | BIRTHDAY-BOOK, stamped in gold; double-line border, blind-stamped. *Spine:* ten lines, blind-stamped. *Back cover:* double-line border, blind-stamped. All edges gilt. Pale yellow endpapers.

Presented by the Friends of the Detroit Public Library.

176. Weatherly, Frederick Edward
THE ILLUSTRATED | CHILDREN'S | BIRTHDAY BOOK. | EDITED AND IN PART WRITTEN, | BY | F. E. WEATHERLY. | With Illustrations by | KATE COLEMAN, KATE GREENAWAY, ROBERT BARNES, | MRS. STAPLES, MISS BENNETT, AND OTHERS. | London: | HENRY FROWDE, AMEN CORNER, E.C.

[ii] [2] 3–288 p. 11.5 cm.

Black morocco. *Front cover:* THE CHILDREN'S | BIRTHDAY BOOK, stamped in gold; single-line border, stamped in gold. *Spine:* THE | CHILDREN'S | BIRTHDAY | BOOK | ILLUS-TRATED, stamped in gold; single-line border top and bottom, stamped in gold. *Back cover:* single-line border, stamped in gold. All edges gilt. Black endpapers.

"The engravings are by Messrs. W. & F. R. Cheshire," p. 286.

"J. Wright & Co. Printers, Bristol," p. 288.

Presentation inscription dated "13th May /96," p. [1] at beginning.

Contains black-and-white illustrations signed "K.G.," pp. 76, 178, 202, 208, and 228, and unsigned black-and-white illustrations by K.G., pp. 24, 72, and 234.

Presented by the Friends of the Detroit Public Library.

177. Weatherly, George Frederick
KATE GREENAWAY'S | MALBUCH | Für das kleine Volk. | Enthält 112 Holzschnitt-Illustrationen zum Coloriren. | Nach Zeichnungen von Kate Greenaway. | Mit beschreibenden Er-zählungen und Reimen von George Weatherly, | Ins Deutsche übersetzt und ergänzt von | Fanny Stockhausen. | Sechste Au-flage. | München. | Theo. Stroefer's Kunstverlag.

[ix] X–XIII, 14–100 [101–4] p. 23.8 cm.

Gray pictorial boards. *Front cover:* KATE GREENAWAY'S | MAL-BUCH | FÜR DAS KLEINE VOLK., printed in gold; picture of girl sitting in field under a tree, holding a palette, printing in blue; vase with flowers and decorative border decorate rest of cover, printed in blue. *Spine:* continues illustration of field, printed in blue. *Back cover:* continues illustration of field with two children looking through high grass at two water birds, printed in blue; decorative border, printed in blue. Pages [i–ii] and [103–4] used as pastedowns.

"Kate Greenaway's Werke... München: Theo. Stroefer," p. [ii] (front pastedown).

Illustrated advertisements for "Theo Stroefer's Kunstverlag in München," pp. [iii–iv] and [101–3].

"Stuttgart. Druck von Gebrüder Kröner," p. [viii].

Colored frontispiece; other illustrations printed in black and white.

Presented by the Friends of the Detroit Public Library.

178. Weatherly, George Frederick
THE "LITTLE FOLKS" | NATURE PAINTING BOOK. | A SERIES OF | OUTLINE ENGRAVINGS FOR WATER-COLOUR PAINTING, | WITH STORIES AND VERSES | BY | GEORGE WEATHERLY. | TWENTY-FIFTH THOUSAND. | CASSELL, PETTER, GALPIN & CO.: | LONDON, PARIS & NEW YORK. | [ALL RIGHTS RESERVED]

[v] vi–x [11] 12–80 [2] 3–[8] [2] p. 22.2 cm.

Green cloth. *Front cover:* THE | LITTLE FOLKS' | NATURE | PAINTING | BOOK, stamped in black and gold; birds, a butterfly, and flowers, stamped in black and gold; single-line border, stamped in black. *Spine:* blank. *Back cover:* decorative device in center and triple-line border, blind-stamped. White endpapers.

"Cassell Petter, Galpin & Co., Belle Sauvage Works, London, E.C. 50,680," p. 80.

Selections from Cassell, Petter, Galpin & Co.'s Publications, pp. [1]–8 at end.

"The following drawing materials are also supplied wholesale by Eyre & Spottiswoode," last 2 pp. at end, tipped in.

Contains unsigned black-and-white illustrations by K.G., pp. [v] 12, 22, 32, 48, 66, and 76.

Presented by the Friends of the Detroit Public Library.

179. Weatherly, George Frederick
THE "LITTLE FOLKS" | PAINTING BOOK. | A SERIES OF | OUTLINE ENGRAVINGS FOR WATER-COLOUR PAINTING, | BY KATE GREENAWAY, | WITH DESCRIPTIVE STORIES AND VERSES BY GEORGE WEATHERLY. | CASSELL PETTER & GALPIN: | LONDON, PARIS & NEW YORK.

[v] vi–ix, 10–96 [2] 3–4 p. 22.5 cm.

Yellow wrappers. *Front cover:* PRICE ONE SHILLING. | (OR ELEGANTLY BOUND IN CLOTH GILT, PRICE TWO SHILLINGS. | THE | "LITTLE FOLKS" | Painting | Book | CASSELL

PETTER & GALPIN: | LONDON, PARIS & NEW YORK., printed in black. *Spine:* rebacked. *Back cover:* advertisement for *Little Folks, The Illustrated Magazine for Children,* published by Cassell Petter & Galpin.

"Books suitable for School Libraries, &c., Selected from Cassell Petter & Galpin's Publications," verso front cover.

Colored frontispiece inserted after p. [ii].

"Cassell Petter & Galpin, Belle Sauvage Works, London, E.C.," p. 96.

Selections from Cassell Petter & Galpin's Publications, pp. [1]–4 at end.

"Selection from Cassell Petter & Galpin's Publications," recto back cover.

Inscription dated "August 17th/79," p. [i].

Presented by John S. Newberry.

180. Weatherly, George Frederick
THE "LITTLE FOLKS" | PAINTING BOOK. | A SERIES OF | OUTLINE ENGRAVINGS FOR WATER-COLOUR PAINTING, | BY KATE GREENAWAY, | WITH DESCRIPTIVE STORIES AND VERSES BY GEORGE WEATHERLY. | CASSELL, PETTER, GALPIN & CO.: | LONDON, PARIS & NEW YORK.

[v] vi–ix, 10–96 [2] 3–[8] p. 22.1 cm.

Red cloth. *Front cover:* THE LITTLE FOLKS' | PAINTING BOOK, stamped in black on a gold background; picture of children painting, stamped in black; double-line border, stamped in black. *Spine:* blank. *Back cover:* decorative device in center and triple-line border, blind-stamped. Cream-colored endpapers.

Colored frontispiece inserted after p. [ii].

"Cassell, Petter, Galpin & Co., Belle Sauvage Works, London E.C. 100,979," p. 96.

Selections from Cassell Petter & Galpin's Publications, pp. [1–8] at end.

Presented by John S. Newberry.

181. Weatherly, George Frederick
THE "LITTLE FOLKS" | PAINTING BOOK. | A SERIES OF | OUTLINE ENGRAVINGS FOR WATER-COLOUR PAINTING, | BY KATE GREENAWAY, | WITH DECORATIVE STORIES AND VERSES BY GEORGE WEATHERLY. | Ninety-third Thousand. | CASSELL, PETTER, GALPIN & CO.: | LONDON, PARIS & NEW YORK.

[v] vi–ix, 10–96 [ii] iii–[viii] p. 22.3 cm.

Green cloth. *Front cover:* same as item 180. *Spine:* blank. *Back cover:* slightly different decorative device from item 180 in center and triple-line border, blind-stamped. White endpapers.

Colored frontispiece inserted after p. [ii].

"Cassell, Petter, Galpin & Co., Belle Sauvage Works, London, E.C. 50,1080," p. 96.

Selections from Cassell, Petter, Galpin & Co.'s Publications, pp. [i–viii] at end.

Advertised as "Just Published," *Pictures to Paint* by Kate Greenaway, Third Edition of *The "Little Folks" Nature Painting Book,* and the Twenty-Fifth Thousand of *The "Little Folks" Black and White Painting Book,* p. [i] at end.

Presented by the Friends of the Detroit Public Library.

182. Weatherly, George Frederick

THE "LITTLE FOLKS" | PAINTING BOOK. | A SERIES OF | OUTLINE ENGRAVINGS FOR WATER-COLOUR PAINTING, | BY KATE GREENAWAY, | WITH DESCRIPTIVE STORIES AND VERSES BY GEORGE WEATHERLY. | SECOND EDITION. | CASSELL PETTER & GALPIN: | LONDON, PARIS & NEW YORK.

[v] vi–ix, 10–96 [2] 3–[8] p. 22.3 cm.

Brown cloth. *Front cover:* same as item 180. *Spine:* blank. *Back cover:* same as item 180. White endpapers.

Colored frontispiece inserted after p. [ii].

"Cassell Petter & Galpin, Belle Sauvage Works, London, E.C.," p. 96.

Selections from Cassell Petter & Galpin's Publications, pp. [1–8] at end.

Presented by the Friends of the Detroit Public Library.

183. Woolsey, Sarah Chauncey

A | GUERNSEY LILY; | OR, | HOW THE FEUD WAS HEALED. | A Story for Girls and Boys. | BY | SUSAN COOLIDGE, | AUTHOR OF "WHAT KATY DID," "THE NEW-YEAR'S BARGAIN," ETC. | BOSTON: | ROBERTS BROTHERS. | 1881.

[ix] x–[xii] [1] 2–238 [2] p.

"Copyright, 1880, by Roberts Brothers" and "University Press: John Wilson and Son, Cambridge," p. [iv].

"University Press: John Wilson & Son, Cambridge," p. 238.

Contains black-and-white illustrations signed "K.G.," pp. 63, 70, 78, 110, 140, 147, 155, 159, and 232.

a. 20.9 cm.

Yellow cloth. *Front cover:* A GUERNSEY LILY | By Susan Coolidge, stamped in gold and black; picture of man and woman looking through a telescope at a fishing boat, with rocks and windmill in background, stamped in black; single-line border, stamped in black. *Spine:* A | GUERNSEY | LILY | BY | SUSAN | COOLIDGE | ROBERTS BROS., stamped in gold and black; decorative flower, stamped in black. *Back cover:* blank. Pictorial endpapers containing advertisements for "Susan Coolidge's Popular Story Books" and a map of the island of Guernsey and the island of Jersey.

Presented by Thekla Hodgson.

b. 20.8 cm.

Dark gray cloth. *Front cover:* same as item 183*a. Spine:* same as item 183*a. Back cover:* blank. Pictorial endpapers with same design as item 183*a.*

Presented by the Friends of the Detroit Public Library.

184.   A Year | of | Golden Days | Illustrated by | HARRIET M. BENNETT, ETC. | LONDON: | J. & A. MACK, 28, PATERNOSTER ROW.

[3] 4–256 p. 10.2 cm.

Yellow cloth. *Front cover:* A Year of | Golden Days, stamped in black; picture of girl and boy holding hands, stamped in black and yellow; sprigs of flowers, stamped in black and yellow. *Spine:* A | Year | of | Golden | Days, stamped in black; decorative flowers, stamped in black. *Back cover:* head and shoulders of small child in circular border with flowers, stamped in black and yellow. White endpapers.

Advertisement for *Songs for the Nursery* and *The Illustrated Children's Birthday Book*, p. 256.

"J. Wright & Co., Printers, Bristol," p. 256.

Presentation inscription dated "Sept. 28th, 1900," front flyleaf.

Contains at least one unsigned black-and-white illustration by K.G. p. 112.

185. Yonge, Charlotte
HEARTSEASE | OR | THE BROTHER'S WIFE | ILLUSTRATED BY KATE GREENAWAY | London | MACMILLAN AND CO. | 1879 | The Right of Translation is Reserved

[xii] [1] 2–548 [1] 2 p. 18.9 cm.

Olive green cloth. *Front cover:* two bands, stamped in gold. *Spine:* CHARLOTTE M. | YONGE | HEARTSEASE | MACMILLAN | & CO., stamped in gold; bands continued from front cover, stamped in gold and black. *Back cover:* bands continued from front cover, blind-stamped. Black endpapers.

"Novels by Charlotte M. Yonge, Macmillan & Co., p. [i] at beginning.

"Novels and Tales by Charlotte M. Yonge. Volume II Heartsease. London, Macmillan and Co., 1879," p. [iii] at beginning.

"London: R. Clay, Sons, and Taylor, Printers," p. 548.

"Works by Charlotte M. Yonge," pp. [1]–2 at end.

The illustration listed in "List of Illustrations" as being at p. 198 is actually used as the frontispiece. The other two illustrations are inserted after pp. 126 and 224.

Presented by the Friends of the Detroit Public Library.

186. Yonge, Charlotte

THE | HEIR OF REDCLYFFE | ILLUSTRATED BY KATE GREENAWAY | London | MACMILLAN AND CO. | 1881 | The Right of Translation is Reserved

[xii] [1] 2–524 [4] p. 18.9 cm.

Olive green cloth. *Front cover:* same as item 185. *Spine:* same as item 185. *Back cover:* same as item 185. Black endpapers.

"Novels by Charlotte M. Yonge, Macmillan & Co.," p. [i].

"Novels and Tales by Charlotte M. Yonge. Volume I The Heir of Redclyffe. London, Macmillan and Co., 1881," p. [iii].

"London: R. Clay, Sons, and Taylor, Printers, Bread Street Hill," p. [iv].

Macmillan & Co. catalogue, pp. [1–4] at end.

The illustration listed in "List of Illustrations" as being at p. 519 is actually used as the frontispiece. The other three illustrations are inserted after pp. 100, 149, and 165.

Presented by the Friends of the Detroit Public Library.

187. Yonge, Charlotte

THE | HEIR OF REDCLYFFE | ILLUSTRATED BY KATE GREENAWAY | London | MACMILLAN AND CO. | AND NEW YORK | 1887 | The Right of Translation is Reserved.

[xii] [1] 2–524 [2] p. 18.9 cm.

Olive green cloth. *Front cover:* same as item 185. *Spine:* CHARLOTTE M. | YONGE | THE HEIR | OF | REDCLYFFE | MACMILLAN | & Co., stamped in gold; bands continued from front cover, stamped in gold and black. *Back cover:* same as item 185. Black endpapers.

"Novels by Charlotte M. Yonge, Macmillan & Co.," p. [i].

"Novels and Tales by Charlotte M. Yonge. Volume I The Heir of Radclyffe, London, Macmillan and Co., and New York, 1887," p. [iii].

"Richard Clay and Sons, London and Bungay," pp. [iv] and 524.

"Macmillan and Co.'s 6s. Popular Novels," pp. [1–2] at end.

The illustration listed in "List of Illustrations" as being at p. 519 is actually used as the frontispiece. The other three illustrations are inserted after pp. 100, 149, and 165.

Presented by the Friends of the Detroit Public Library.

188.* Zimmern, Helen

TALES FROM THE EDDA | TOLD BY | HELEN ZIMMERN. | WITH ILLUSTRATIONS BY | KATE GREENAWAY & OTHERS. | London: | W. SWAN SONNENSCHEIN & Co. | PATERNOSTER ROW.

a. [ix] x [1] 2–146 [1]–12 p. 18.0 cm.

Green cloth. *Front cover:* TALES | FROM THE | EDDA, stamped in gold; wheat, stars, and a bird, stamped in black; single-line border, stamped in black. *Spine:* TALES | FROM | THE | EDDA | ZIMMERN, stamped in gold; decorative device and wheat, stamped in black. *Back cover:* geometric device and triple-line border, blind-stamped. All edges gilt. Green and white floral endpapers.

"Paternoster Row, October, 1882. New books for presents and prizes for the season 1882–3 published by W. Swan Sonnenschein & Co.," pp. [1]–12 at end.

Contains black-and-white illustrations signed by K.G., pp. [iv, 97, and 127].

Presented by the Friends of the Detroit Public Library.

b. [ix] x [1] 2–146 p. 18.1 cm.

Red cloth. *Front cover:* TALES | FROM THE | EDDA, stamped in gold; flowers and leaves, stamped in gold, green, and black. *Spine:* TALES | FROM | THE | EDDA | ZIMMERN, stamped in gold; decorative device, stamped in black. *Back cover:* blank. All edges gilt. White endpapers.

Contains black-and-white illustrations signed by K.G., pp. [iv, 97, and 127].

Presented by the Friends of the Detroit Public Library.

*Illustrated.

118

188. Frontispiece, *Tales from the Edda*.

234. Illustration for "The Little Big Woman and The Big Little Girl," *St. Nicholas Magazine*, April 1879.

225. Illustration for "Bebel," *People's Magazine*, 1873.

MAGAZINES AND ANNUALS

Magazines and annuals are presented somewhat differently than were the books in the previous section. Although the title, place of publication, publisher, volume number, and date of each item are recorded exactly as they appear, no attempt has been made to simulate the title page. Page numbers, size, and description of the binding have not been included because many items have been rebound or are individual issues with no binding. Peculiarities of the copies have not been noted unless they pertain to illustrations by K.G. Bracketed material is information not found anywhere in the item and supplied by the compiler.

189.   Babyland. Edited by the Editors of Wide Awake. Boston, D. Lothrop & Co., Vol. 6, no. 9, Sept. 1882.
        Wrappers.
        Contains unsigned black-and-white illustration by K.G., p. 73.
        Presented by the Friends of the Detroit Public Library.

190.   Babyland. Edited by the Editors of Wide Awake. Boston, D. Lothrop & Co., Vol. 7, no. 2, Feb. 1883.
        Wrappers.
        Contains black-and-white illustration signed "K.G.," front cover, and unsigned black-and-white illustration by K.G., p. 84.
        Presented by the Friends of the Detroit Public Library.

191.   The English Illustrated Magazine. London, The Illustrated London News, Ltd., Vol. 12, Oct. 1894–March 1895.
        Blue cloth.
        Contains colored illustration "A Sailor's Wife. Kate Greenaway," frontispiece to the Christmas Number, December, 1894.
        Presented by the Friends of the Detroit Public Library.

192.   The English Illustrated Magazine. London, Ingram Brothers, Christmas Number, 1898.
        Wrappers.
        Contains colored illustration "Primroses.—By Kate Greenaway" between pp. 320 and 321.
        Presented by the Friends of the Detroit Public Library.

193. The Girl's Own Annual. Vol. 8. London, 1887.
Contains "The Girl's Own Paper," vol. VIII, no. 353, Oct. 2, 1886–vol. VIII, no. 404, Sept. 24, 1887.
Contains colored illustration "Afternoon Tea. From the Drawing by Kate Greenaway," frontispiece, and colored title page signed "K.G."
a. Blue cloth.
Presented by the Friends of the Detroit Public Library.

b. Green cloth.
Presented by the Friends of the Detroit Public Library.

194. The Girl's Own Annual. Vol. 12. London, 1891.
Contains "The Girl's Own Paper," vol. XII, no. 562, Oct. 4, 1890–vol. XII, no. 613, Sept. 26, 1891.
Contains colored illustration "Garland Day. Drawn by Kate Greenaway," frontispiece, and colored title page signed "K.G."
a. Blue cloth, beveled boards.
"Garland Day. Drawn by Kate Greenaway," with note: "This outline impression to be painted in water-colours by our readers in imitation of the fully-coloured plate in our previous monthly part.... Examiners: —Miss Kate Greenaway and The Editor of 'The Girl's Own Paper.'...," inserted after p. 144.
Presented by the Friends of the Detroit Public Library.

b. Brown cloth, beveled boards.
"Garland Day. Drawn by Kate Greenaway," with note: "This outline impression to be painted in water-colours by our readers in imitation of the fully-coloured plate in our previous monthly part.... Examiners: —Miss Kate Greenaway and The Editor of 'The Girl's Own Paper.'...," inserted before frontispiece.
Presented by the Friends of the Detroit Public Library.

195. The Girl's Own Annual. Vol. 13. London, 1891.
Green cloth.
Contains "The Girl's Own Paper," vol. 13, no. 614, Oct. 3, 1891–vol. 13, no. 665, Sept. 24, 1892.
Contains colored illustration "Golden Summer. From the painting by Kate Greenaway" between pp. 106 and 107.
Presented by the Friends of the Detroit Public Library.

196. The Girl's Own Paper. London, Part 82, Nov. 1886.
Wrappers.
Contains the numbers for October, 1886.

Contains colored illustration "Afternoon Tea. From the drawing by Kate Greenaway," frontispiece.
Presented by the Friends of the Detroit Public Library.

197.   The Girl's Own Paper. London, Part 93, Oct. 1887.
Wrappers.
Contains the numbers for September, 1887.
Contains added colored title page for the *Girl's Own Annual,* signed "K. G."
Presented by the Friends of the Detroit Public Library.

198.   The Girl's Own Paper. London, Part 143, Dec., 1891.
Wrappers.
Contains the numbers for November, 1891.
Contains colored illustration "Golden Summer. From the painting by Kate Greenaway," frontispiece.
Presented by the Friends of the Detroit Public Library.

199.   The Girl's Own Paper. London, Dec. 1901.
Wrappers. Covers lacking.
Contains colored illustration "A Specimen Page of Miss Kate Greenaway's Work. From the 'Pied Piper of Hamelin' (F. Warne & Co.)," frontispiece, and four black-and-white illustrations signed "K.G.," pp. 197–98 (these illustrations accompany an article on Kate Greenaway and are described as hitherto unpublished).
Presented by the Friends of the Detroit Public Library.

200.   The Graphic. London, Summer Number, 1878.
Wrappers.
Contains nine black-and-white illustrations signed "K.G." for "Our babies among the buttercups and on the Seashore," p. 23.
Presented by the Friends of the Detroit Public Library.

201.   Harper's Young People. New York, Harper & Brothers, Vol. 1, no. 1–26, Nov. 4, 1879–April 27, 1880.
Red cloth.
Contains six unsigned black-and-white illustrations by K.G., p. 40, and black-and-white illustration "One Hundred Years Ago.—Drawn by Kate Greenaway," p. 81.

202.   Harper's Young People. New York, Harper & Brothers, Vol. 2, no. 53–78, Nov. 2, 1880–April 26, 1881.
Red cloth.

Contains unsigned black-and-white illustrations, possibly by K.G., pp. 16 and 28.

203.   Harper's Young People. New York, Harper & Brothers, Vol. 2, no. 79–104, May 3–Oct. 25, 1881.
Red cloth.
Contains unsigned black-and-white illustrations by K.G., pp. 501 and 653.

204.   Harper's Young People. New York, Harper & Brothers, Vol. 3, no. 131–157, May 2–Oct. 31, 1882.
Red cloth.
Contains unsigned black-and-white illustrations by K.G., pp. 477 and 528.

205.   Harper's Young People. New York, Harper & Brothers, Vol. 4, no. 158–182, Nov. 7, 1882–April 24, 1883.
Red cloth.
Contains unsigned black-and-white illustration, possibly by K.G., p. 340, and unsigned black-and-white illustration by K.G., "Grandmamma's School-Days," p. 361.

206.   Harper's Young People. New York, Harper & Brothers, Vol. 4, no. 183–209, May 1–Oct. 30, 1883.
Red cloth.
Contains black-and-white illustration signed "K.G." for "Home Beauty," a poem by Austin Dobson, p. 541, and nine unsigned black-and-white illustrations by K.G., p. 832.

207.   Harper's Young People. New York, Harper & Brothers, Vol. 5, no. 210–235, Nov. 6, 1883–April 29, 1884.
Red cloth.
Contains unsigned black-and-white illustrations by K.G., "The Four Seasons," p. 14, and pp. 142–43, 206, and 222, and an unsigned black-and-white illustration, possibly by K.G., p. 62.

208.   Harper's Young People. New York, Harper & Brothers, Vol. 5, no. 236–261, May 6–Oct. 28, 1884.
Red cloth.
Contains unsigned black-and-white illustration by K.G., p. 478.

209.   Holly Leaves. The Christmas Number of the Illustrated Sporting & Dramatic News. London, Vol. 32, no. 838 & 839, 1889.
Wrappers.

Contains black-and-white illustration "Preparing for Christmas, By Kate Greenaway," p. 5.
Presented by the Friends of the Detroit Public Library.

210. The Illustrated London News. London, Vol. 65, no. 1846, Dec. 26, 1874.
Wrappers.
Contains black-and-white illustration "A Christmas Dream. Drawn by Kate Greenaway," p. 605.
Presented by the Friends of the Detroit Public Library.

211. The Illustrated London News. London, Christmas Number, 1877.
Wrappers.
Contains black-and-white illustrations "Little Loves. Drawn by Kate Greenaway," p. [1], and "Three Home Rulers. Drawn by Kate Greenaway," p. 4.
Presented by the Friends of the Detroit Public Library.

212. The Illustrated London News. London, Vol. 72, no. 2021, March 23, 1878.
Wrappers.
Contains black-and-white illustration "Darby and Joan. By Kate Greenaway," front cover.
Presented by John S. Newberry.

213. The Illustrated London News. London, Christmas Number, 1879.
Wrappers.
Contains colored illustration "Christmas at Little-Peopleton Manor. From Drawings by Kate Greenaway,"pp. [36–37].
Presented by the Friends of the Detroit Public Library.

214. The Illustrated London News. London, Christmas Number, 1880.
Wrappers.
Contains colored illustration signed "K.G.," front cover, and unsigned colored illustration by K.G., p. 24.
Presented by the Friends of the Detroit Public Library.

215. The Illustrated London News. London, Christmas Number, 1882.
Wrappers.

Contains black-and-white illustration "We Wish You a Merry Christmas Drawn by Kate Greenaway," front cover.
Presented by the Friends of the Detroit Public Library.

216.   The Ladies' Home Journal. Philadelphia, The Curtis Publishing Co., Vol. 12, no. 4, March, 1895.
        Wrappers.
        Contains black-and-white illustration signed "K.G.," p. 31.
        Presented by the Friends of the Detroit Public Library.

217.   The Ladies' Home Journal. Philadelphia, The Curtis Publishing Co., Vol. 12, no. 5, April, 1895.
        Wrappers.
        Contains black-and-white illustrations "Kate Greenaway's April Children. Pictures by Miss Greenaway; Verses by Laura E. Richards," p. 13.
        Presented by the Friends of the Detroit Public Library.

218.   The Ladies' Home Journal. Philadelphia, The Curtis Publishing Co., Vol. 13, no. 1, Dec., 1895.
        Wrappers.
        Contains black-and-white illustrations "Maidie's Dance. Drawings by Kate Greenaway. Verses by Laura E. Richards," p. 17.
        Presented by the Friends of the Detroit Public Library.

219.   Little Wide Awake. An Illustrated Magazine for Good Children. Edited by Mrs. Sale Barker. London & New York, George Routledge & Sons, 1881.
        Boards.
        Contains colored illustration "A Morning Call. From a Drawing by Kate Greenaway," frontispiece and repeated on front cover, and black-and-white illustration "Gathering Flowers in May," signed "K.G.," p. 136.
        Presented by the Friends of the Detroit Public Library.

220.   Little Wide Awake. An Illustrated Magazine for Good Children. Edited by Mrs. Sale Barker. London & New York, George Routledge & Sons, 1882.
        Turquoise cloth.
        Contains colored illustration "Prissy. From a drawing by Kate Greenaway," frontispiece. Head and shoulders of "Prissy" repeated on front cover.
        Presented by John S. Newberry.

221.   Little Wide-Awake. A Coloured Annual for Children. By Mrs.
        Sale Barker. London & New York, George Routledge & Sons,
        1884.
        Blue cloth.
        Contains colored illustration signed "K.G.," p. [49].
        Presented by John S. Newberry.

222.   Little Wide-Awake. An Illustrated Magazine for Children.
        Edited by Mrs. Sale Barker. London & New York, George Rout-
        ledge & Sons, 1885.
        Contains colored illustration "Early Primrose. From a Draw-
        ing by Kate Greenaway.," frontispiece.
        a. Blue cloth.
        Presented by the Friends of the Detroit Public Library.

        b. Boards.
        Presented by the Friends of the Detroit Public Library.

223.   Little Wide-Awake. An Illustrated Magazine for Children.
        Edited by Mrs. Sale Barker. London & New York, George Rout-
        ledge & Sons, 1889.
        Boards.
        Contains colored illustration "A School Girl. From a Picture
        by Kate Greenaway," frontispiece.
        Presented by the Friends of the Detroit Public Library.

224.   The Magazine of Art. London, Paris & New York, Cassell,
        Petter, Galpin & Co., n.s., part 31, May 1883.
        Wrappers.
        Contains black-and-white illustration signed "K.G." for
        "Home Beauty," a poem by Austin Dobson, p. [277].
        Presented by the Friends of the Detroit Public Library.

225.*   The People's Magazine: An Illustrated Miscellany for Family
        Reading. New Series. London, Vol. 11, no. 61–66, Jan.–June,
        1873.
        Brown cloth.
        Contains unsigned black-and-white illustrations by K.G., pp.
        24 and 97.
        Presented by the Friends of the Detroit Public Library.

226.   Routledge's Christmas Number. London & New York,
        George Routledge & Sons [1881]

*Illustrated.

Wrappers.

Contains colored illustration "Little Fanny," signed "Kate Greenaway," frontispiece.

Presented by the Friends of the Detroit Public Library.

227. Routledge's Every Girl's Annual. Edited by Miss Alicia A. Leith. London, George Routledge & Sons, 1878.

Introduction dated "London 1878," p.v.

Contains colored illustration "Fun and Frolic at Beauchamp Towers," signed "K.G.," frontispiece, and colored title page signed "K.G."

a. Brown cloth.

Presented by the Friends of the Detroit Public Library.

b. Dark red cloth.

Presented by John S. Newberry.

228. Routledge's Every Girl's Annual. Edited by Miss Alicia A. Leith. London, George Routledge & Sons, 1880.

Blue cloth.

Contains colored illustration signed "K.G.," frontispiece, and colored title page signed "K.G."

Presented by John S. Newberry.

229. Routledge's Every Girl's Annual. Edited by Miss Alicia A. Leith. London, George Routledge & Sons, 1881.

Blue cloth.

Contains colored illustration signed "K.G.," frontispiece, and colored title page signed "K.G."

Presented by the Friends of the Detroit Public Library.

230. Routledge's Every Girl's Annual. Edited by Miss Alicia A. Leith. London, George Routledge & Sons, 1882.

Blue cloth.

Contains colored illustration signed "K.G.," frontispiece, and colored title page signed "K.G."

Presented by the Friends of the Detroit Public Library.

231. St. Nicholas: Scribner's Illustrated Magazine for Girls and Boys. Conducted by Mary Mapes Dodge. New York, Scribner & Co., Vol. V, Nov. 1877–Nov. 1878.

Red cloth.

Contains an unsigned black-and-white "Christmas Card" by K.G., p. 91, and a black-and-white "New-Year Card. (Drawn by Miss L. [sic] Greenaway.)," p. 182.

232.   St. Nicholas. New York, Scribner & Co.; London, Sampson, Low, Marston & Co., Vol. VI, no. 3, Jan. 1879.
        Wrappers.
        Contains twelve black-and-white illustrations signed "K.G." for "Children's Day at St. Paul's," by N. D'Anvers, pp. 148–55.
        Presented by the Friends of the Detroit Public Library.

233.   St. Nicholas. New York, Scribner & Co.; London, Sampson, Low, Marston & Co., Vol. VI, no. 5, March, 1879.
        Wrappers.
        Contains unsigned black-and-white illustration by K.G. for "Calling the Flowers," by M. M. D., p. 333.
        Presented by the Friends of the Detroit Public Library.

234.*   St. Nicholas. New York, Scribner & Co.; London, Sampson, Low, Marston & Co., Vol. VI, no. 6, April, 1879.
        Wrappers.
        Contains unsigned black-and-white illustration by K.G. for "The Little Big Woman and The Big Little Girl," by M. M. D., p. 383, and four black-and-white illustrations by K.G. for "Beating the Bounds," by Thomas Hughes, pp. 392–95.
        Presented by the Friends of the Detroit Public Library.

235.   St. Nicholas: Scribner's Illustrated Magazine for Girls and Boys. Conducted by Mary Mapes Dodge. New York, Scribner & Co., Vol. VI, Nov. 1878–Nov. 1879.
        Red cloth.
        Contains twelve black-and-white illustrations signed "K.G." for "Children's Day at St. Paul's," by N. D'Anvers, pp. 148–55, an unsigned black-and-white illustration by K.G. for "Calling the Flowers," by M. M. D., p. 333, an unsigned black-and-white illustration by K.G. for "The Little Big Woman and the Big Little Girl," by M. M. D., p. 383, and four black-and-white illustrations by K.G. for "Beating the Bounds," by Thomas Hughes, pp. 392–95.

236.   St. Nicholas: Scribner's Illustrated Magazine for Girls and Boys. Conducted by Mary Mapes Dodge. New York, Scribner & Co., Vol. VII, Nov. 1879–Nov. 1880.
        Red cloth.
        Contains black-and-white illustration signed "K.G.," for "The Family With Whom Everything Went Wrong," by M. M. D., p. 32, and black-and-white illustration signed "K.G." for "Seeing is Believing," by J. S., p. 336.

*Illustrated.

CALENDARS, CARDS, ETC.

In this section title, place of publication, publisher, and date are given when they are known. Bracketed material is information not found anywhere in the item and supplied by the compiler. Many items have no title; in such cases titles have been supplied from the published work in which the illustrations appear, if they have been identified, from Carroll Alton Means' articles on K.G. cards (see the Selected Bibliography for a listing of his articles on these cards in *Hobbies*), or from other sources. If no title could be provided in this way, one has been supplied by the compiler.

237. [The April Baby's Book of Tunes]
    5 cards
    Each card contains a colored illustration by K.G. from *The April Baby's Book of Tunes*, printed on heavy cardboard.
    Card 1. 16.8 x 17.6 cm. Six-line poem, "Little Polly Flinders," recto. Size of illustration: 9.1 x 7.8 cm.
    Card 2. 16.2 x 17.1 cm. " 'But Flinders' Foots was cold,' " recto. Size of illustration: 12.7 x 13.0 cm.
    Card 3. 16.7 x 17.5 cm. "The Strains of 'Polly Flinders,' " recto. Size of illustration: 12.8 x 13.0 cm.
    Card 4. 17.5 x 17.9 cm. Six-line poem, "Little Miss Muffet," recto. Size of illustration: 7.5 x 8.5 cm.
    Card 5. 15.5 x 17.4 cm. Four-line poem, "Jack and Jill," recto. Size of illustration: 12.8 x 9.6 cm.
    From the collection of Robert Partridge.
    Presented by the Friends of the Detroit Public Library.

238. Bookplate.
    9.1 x 7.4 cm.
    Bookplate designed by K.G. for Frederick Locker showing two children seated under a tree from which hangs a coat-of-arms; owl in background; floral border. Motto: "Fear God & Fear Nought."
    Printed in black and white.
    Signed "K.G."

239. Bookplate.
    9.1 x 6.8 cm.

Bookplate designed by K.G. for Godfrey Locker-Lampson showing young boy in long fur-trimmed coat holding a book, coat-of-arms in the background. Motto: "Fear God and Fear Nought."

Printed in brown and white.

Signed "K.G."

240. Bookplate.

13.0 x 9.8 cm.

Bookplate designed by K.G. for Oliver Stillingfleet Locker Lampson showing side view of woman in long dress carrying a bowl of flowers. Motto: "Fear God Fear Nought." Dated "1898."

Printed in black and white.

Signed "K.G."

Holograph signature: "Mrs. Locker Lampson June 11/98."

241. Bookplate.

12.3 x 9.8 cm.

Bookplate designed by K.G. for Victoria Alexandrina Mary Cecil Herbert showing two women and three children seated on the ground; one woman holds an open book; trees in background.

Printed in black and white.

Signed "K.G."

242. [Briggs & Co.'s Patent Transferring Papers]

11.4 x 7.2 cm.

Trade card printed in colors containing illustration, possibly by K.G., from Briggs' *Patent Transferring Papers*, p. 145, "Scandal." "Alike, the World Over" and twelve-line dialogue and "Moral" between Minnie and Carrie, recto; advertisement for C. I. Hood & Co., Apothecaries, verso.

243. Button.

4.0 cm. in diameter.

Metal button depicting illustration by K.G. of two children on a seesaw, in high relief.

Presented by the Friends of the Detroit Public Library.

244. Button.

2.0 cm. in diameter.

Metal button depicting illustration by K.G. of little boy blowing a horn, in low relief.

Presented by the Friends of the Detroit Public Library.

245. Button.
4.5 cm. in diameter.
Metal button depicting illustration by K.G. of boy and girl sitting on a fence under an umbrella, in high relief.
Presented by the Friends of the Detroit Public Library.

246. Calendar 1875. [London] Marcus Ward & Co.
[8] p., including covers. Oblong. 7.5 x 10.4 cm.
Printed on stiff paper.
Contains four unsigned illustrations by K.G., printed in gold and colors, pp. [1, 4, 5, and 8].
Presented by John S. Newberry.

247. Calendar of the Months, 1884. London, Belfast & New York, Marcus Ward & Company.
[12] p., including covers. 11.3 cm.
Printed on stiff paper.
"Designed by Thomas Crane" and "The Figures by Kate Greenaway," p. [1].
Contains twelve unsigned colored illustrations by K.G.
Presented by John S. Newberry.

248. [Calendar of the Months, February 1884. London] Marcus Ward & Co.
Oblong. 9.0 x 12.7 cm.
Greeting card, printed in colors, containing unsigned illustration by K.G. of February (boy in green coat with umbrella and letter) from *Calendar of the Months, 1884;* 0.3-cm. gold border. "Christmas" and poem beginning "For whom have you brought a letter," recto; "F" in "For" is composed of tree branches.

249. [Calendar of the Months, April and May 1884. London] Marcus Ward & Co.
2 cards. Oblong. 10.3 × 14.2 cm.
Greeting cards, printed in colors, containing unsigned illustrations by K.G. of April and May from *Calendar of the Months, 1884;* an approximately 0.5-cm., 4-line, pink border.
Card 1. April (girl in orange dress carrying open umbrella). "New Year" and poem beginning "Winsome child of joy!" recto; "W" in "Winsome" composed of pink ribbon.
Card 2. May (back view of girl carrying a basket of flowers). "A Merry Christmas" and poem beginning "Bear my greeting, little maid," recto; "B" in "Bear" composed of blue ribbon.

250. Calendar of the Seasons for 1876. London & Belfast, Marcus Ward & Co.

    [8] p., including covers. 9.8 cm.

    Printed on stiff paper.

    Contains four unsigned illustrations by K.G., printed in gold and colors, pp. [1, 4, 5, and 8].

    Presented by John S. Newberry.

251. Calendar of the Seasons for 1877. London & Belfast, Marcus Ward & Co.

    [8] p., including covers. 10.1 cm.

    Printed on stiff paper.

    Contains at least two unsigned illustrations by K.G., printed in gold and colors, pp. [1 and 8].

    Copy imperfect, lacking pp. [3–6].

    From the collection of Robert Partridge.

    Presented by the Friends of the Detroit Public Library.

252. [Calendar of the Seasons for 1877. London] Marcus Ward & Co.

    3 of 4 cards. 9.5 x 6.5 cm.

    Greeting cards, printed in gold and colors, containing unsigned illustrations by K.G. from *Calendar of the Seasons for 1877*; 0.4-cm. scalloped edge.

    Card 1. Spring (boy and girl holding a nest of eggs). "A Happy New Year Be Before Thee," recto.

    Card 2. Summer (boy and girl playing by the sea shore). "May your Christmas be as Happy," recto.

    Card 3. Fall. Missing.

    Card 4. Winter (boy presenting bouquet of flowers to girl with dog). "A Merry Christmas to You," recto.

253. Calendar of the Seasons, 1881. London & Belfast, Marcus Ward & Co.

    [8] p., including covers. 10.4 cm.

    Printed on stiff paper.

    Contains four unsigned illustrations by K.G., printed in gold and colors, pp. [1, 4, 5, and 8].

    Presented by John S. Newberry.

254. [Calendar of the Seasons, Spring and Winter 1881. London] Marcus Ward & Co.

    3 cards. Oblong. 7.7 x 8.9 cm.

    Greeting cards, printed in colors, containing unsigned illustrations by K.G., two of which are from the *Calendar of the Seasons, 1881*; 2-cm. white and gold border.

Card 1. Spring (front view of three hatted and muffed girls).

a. "Please wait for a moment, don't hurry so fast: / I bring the best greeting altho' I come last," recto; Christmas poem beginning "Sweet maidens," verso.

b. "We come the pretty speech to say / We learned for you on Christmas day," recto; Christmas poem beginning "Where do you go my maidens," verso.

c. No printing.

d. Folding card, [4] p. Illustration and "Honest work and hearty play, / May they cheer you every day!," p. [1]; birthday poem beginning "And are you out of school at last?," pp. [2–3]; 0.2-cm. gold border, p. [4].

Card 2. Winter (back view of three hatted and muffed girls).

a. "Onward brave hearts, o'er the snow-whitened land; / Fair in the distance the blue mountains stand," recto; best wishes poem beginning "A far range of mountains," verso.

b. Folding card, [4] p. Illustration and "Love that speaks from eyes to eyes / needs no tongue, and owns no skies," p. [1]; Valentine poem beginning, "Who will may choose," pp. [2–3]; 0.2-cm. gold border, p. [4].

Card 3 (two girls sitting).

a. "Christmas is the time to greet / With good wishes all we meet," recto; Christmas poem beginning "Christmas is the time to greet," verso.

b. "Quite a picture of friendship, idyllic and sweet; / Only they should be we, dear; it then were complete," recto; New Year poem beginning "Two happy friends," verso.

255. [Calendar of the Seasons, Summer 1881. London] Marcus Ward & Co.

9.1 x 7.5 cm.

Greeting card, printed in colors, containing unsigned illustration by K.G. of girl in pink holding a basket of flowers, rose bush in background from *Calendar of the Seasons, 1881*; 0.2-cm. white border. "I wish you a merry Christmas," recto; inscription dated "Xmas 1883," verso.

256. [Calendar of the Seasons, Autumn 1881. London] Marcus Ward & Co.

Greeting card, printed in colors, containing unsigned illustration by K.G. of girl in pink holding open umbrella, climbing vine in background, from *Calendar of the Seasons, 1881*.

a. 10.6 x 7.4 cm. 0.2-cm. gold border. Birthday poem beginning "O sweet little maid," verso.

b. 10.7 x 7.5 cm. 0.3-cm. gold border. "Luck go with you

pretty lass, / stoop and kiss me as you pass," recto; New Year's greeting poem beginning "Little maiden," verso.

257. Calendar of the Seasons, 1882. London & Belfast, Marcus Ward & Co.

[8] p., including covers. 10.9 cm.

Printed on stiff paper.

Contains four illustrations signed "K.G.," printed in gold and colors, pp. [1, 4, 5 and 8].

From the collection of Robert Partridge.

Presented by the Friends of the Detroit Public Library.

258. [Children by the Pond. London] Marcus Ward and Co.

2 of 4 cards.

Greeting cards, printed in gold and colors, containing unsigned colored illustrations by K.G.

Card 1. "Duck pond." Missing.

Card 2. "Floral arch." Missing.

Card 3. "Three girls." 13.7 x 8.1 cm. 2.6-cm. decorative gold border, top and bottom; 1.2-cm. decorative gold border, sides.

a. "Wishing you the Compliments of the Season," recto.

b. "Health and Happiness be yours Throughout the coming year," recto; inscription dated "Christmas 1880," verso.

Card 4. "Bird's nest." 13.5 x 7.9 cm. 2.4-cm. decorative gold border, top and bottom; 1-cm. decorative gold border, sides. "A Merry Christmas To my Friend," recto; inscription dated "December 24, '78," verso.

Titles for items 258–59 assigned by Means.

259. [Children by the Pond, Three Girls]

[4] p. 18.9 x 15.0 cm.

Greeting card, printed in gold and colors (12.1 x 8.5 cm.), mounted on white lace paper (17.2 x 13.9 cm.), containing unsigned illustration by K.G. of three girls from the set of cards entitled "Children by the Pond," p. [1]; poem, "The Serenade," p. [3].

260. [Children in the manner of Sir Joshua Reynolds' time. London] Marcus Ward & Co.

2 of 4 cards. 13.2 x 9.0 cm.

Greeting cards, printed in gold and colors, containing unsigned illustrations by K.G.; 1-cm. gold and blue decorative border.

Card 1 (girl with fan). "Let me whisper in your ear / A promise from the kind New Year," recto; New Year poem beginning

"What the New Year's bringing," verso.

Card 2 (girl with muff). "A Little messenger I send / with greetings for a little friend," recto; Christmas poem beginning "I said to this gentle maiden," verso.

Cards 3 and 4. Missing.

261. [Children in Ulsters. London] Marcus Ward & Co.
1 of 3 cards. 14.7 x 7.5 cm.
Greeting card, printed in gold and colors, containing un-signed illustration by K.G.; 2.5-cm. bottom border.
Card 1. "Maiden in green ulster." Missing.
Card 2. "Maiden in red ulster." Missing.
Card 3. "Boy in blue ulster." "I come to wish you health & happiness," recto; inscription dated "1880," verso.
Titles assigned by Means.

262. [Children on Flowers. London] Marcus Ward & Co.
4 cards. 12.0 x 9.0 cm.
Greeting cards, printed in gold and colors, containing un-signed illustrations by K.G.; 1.5-cm. decorative gold border.
Card 1. "Daffodil." Christmas poem beginning "Christmas Greetings maiden fair," verso.
Card 2. "Flowering Thorn." New Year's poem beginning "Amid the Peach flowers," verso.
Card 3. "Pansy." Christmas poem beginning "What! sound asleep in a pansy!," verso.
Card 4. "Primrose." New Year's poem beginning "What have we here?," verso.
Titles for items 262–64 assigned by Means.

263. [Children on Flowers. London] Marcus Ward & Co.
1 of 4 cards. 14.0 x 10.0 cm.
Greeting card, printed in gold and colors, containing un-signed illustration by K.G.; 1-cm. decorative scalloped gold border.
Card 1. "Daffodil." Missing.
Card 2. "Flowering Thorn." Missing.
Card 3. "Pansy." Christmas poem beginning "What! sound asleep in a pansy," verso.
Card 4. "Primrose." Missing.

264. [Children on Flowers] Philadelphia, Sunshine Publishing Co.
4 cards. 13.4 x 8.5 cm.
Trade cards, printed in colors, containing unsigned illus-trations by K.G.; 0.2-cm. white border.

Card 1. "Daffodil."
    a. "Compliments of the Camden & Philada. Soap Co... ,"
recto.
    b. "Johnston, Smith & Clancy... ," recto.
Card 2. "Flowering Thorn." "Curtis's Bazaar... ," recto.
Card 3. "Pansy." "Curtis's Bazaar... ," recto.
Card 4. "Primrose." "Curtis's Bazaar... ," recto.

265. [Children's Heads. London] Marcus Ward & Co.
    2 of 3 cards. 9.5 x 9.5 cm.
    Greeting cards, printed in gold and colors, containing signed
illustrations by K.G.; 2.2-cm. decorative border.
    Card 1. "Girl with floral wreath." Missing.
    Card 2. "Boy with hat." Decorative border printed in blue and
gold.
        a. "With the Best of Good Wishes," recto.
        b. "To wish you a Merry Christmas," recto.
    Card 3. "Girl with bonnet." Decorative border printed in pink
and gold; "A very Happy New Year to You," recto.
    Titles assigned by Means.

266. [Coachman Set. London] Marcus Ward & Co.
    2 of 3 cards.
    Greeting cards, printed in colors, containing signed illus-
trations by K.G.; illustration in oval frame with beige border.
    Card 1. "Coachman with crop in hand." Oval cut-out of bor-
der; New Year's greeting, verso.
    Card 2. "Girl in blue dress throwing kiss." 15.0 x 10.7 cm.
"Greeting," recto; New Year's greeting, verso.
    Card 3. "Boy in pink coat and tricorner hat waving." Missing.
    Titles for items 266–67 assigned by Means.

267. [Coachman Set. Boy in tricorner hat waving]
    14.5 x 10.0 cm. on 22.5 x 22.0 cm. sheet.
    Proof of greeting card, printed in black and white, containing
illustration signed "K.G." of "Boy in Tricorner hat waving"
from the set of cards entitled "Coachman Set."
    Contains holograph instructions to the engraver in an un-
known hand.
    Presented by the Friends of the Detroit Public Library.

268. Collecting Card for the Children's Memorial to Kate Greenaway.
    [4] p. 25.2 x 19.5 cm.
    Title taken from p. [1]; pp. [2–3] contain numbered lines for

subscribers' names; p. [4] lists the names of the committee.

"This card to be returned with the amount collected to the Hon. Treasurer, 'Kate Greenaway Memorial Fund,'" p. [3].

Contains three previously published colored illustrations by K.G.

Presented by the Friends of the Detroit Public Library.

269. [Concert Program. London] Marcus Ward & Co.

[4] p., including covers. 10.8 cm.

Printed on stiff paper.

"Concert Hall, Blackheath. Monday & Tuesday 10th & 11th December, 1883," p. [1].

a. Contains unsigned colored illustration by K.G. of Summer (girl in pink holding basket of flowers, rosebush in background) from *Calendar of the Seasons, 1881,* p. [1].

Presented by John S. Newberry.

b. Contains unsigned colored illustration by K.G. of Autumn (girl in pink holding open umbrella, climbing vine in background) from *Calendar of the Seasons, 1881,* p. [1].

Presented by John S. Newberry.

270.* Feed My Lambs. Twelve text-cards for the little ones. With drawings by Kate Greenaway. London, Belfast & New York, Marcus Ward & Co.

12 cards. Oblong. 6.0 x 9.6 cm.

In light blue envelope, with title and unsigned illustration by K.G. of small girl in bonnet and fur-trimmed coat, printed in dark blue.

Title taken from envelope. "No. 172" above title.

Contains six different unsigned colored illustrations by K.G.

Card 1 (little girl in pink coat and white hat). Scripture text beginning "He shall gather," recto.

Card 2 (same illustration as card 1). Scripture text beginning "Suffer little children," recto.

Card 3 (girl in green coat and straw hat holding a large rose). Scripture text beginning "Keep thy father's commandment," recto.

Card 4 (same illustration as card 3). Scripture text beginning "Hearken unto Me," recto.

Card 5 (young girl standing, in pink and white dress holding closed umbrella and young boy seated, in blue suit). Scripture text beginning "Children, obey your parents," recto.

Card 6 (same illustration as card 5). Scripture text beginning "My little children," recto.

Card 7 (girl in red dress holding a bouquet of flowers). Scripture text beginning "Honour thy father and mother," recto.

Card 8 (same illustration as card 7). Scripture text beginning "Remember now thy Creator," recto.

Card 9 (two girls, one in blue polka-dot dress, the other in mustard color dress). Scripture text beginning "Be ye kind," recto.

Card 10 (same illustration as card 9). Scripture text beginning "Be ye therefore followers," recto.

Card 11 (small child in long brown dress and cape, straw hat). Scripture text beginning "I love them," recto.

Card 12 (same illustration as card 11). Scripture text beginning "Children obey your parents," recto.

Presented by the Friends of the Detroit Public Library.

[Feed My Lambs. London] Marcus Ward & Co.

5 cards. Oblong. 9.0 x 12.7 cm.

Greeting cards, printed in colors, containing unsigned illustrations by K.G. from *Feed My Lambs*; 0.3-cm. gold border.

Card 1 (little girl in pink coat and white hat). "New Year" and poem beginning "Softly, lightly the little feet go," recto; "S" in "Softly" composed of a pink ribbon.

Card 2 (girl in green coat and straw hat holding a large rose). "A Happy New Year" and poem beginning "Pick the flowers while you may," recto; "P" in "Pick" composed of a blue ribbon.

Card 3 (young girl standing, in pink and white dress, holding closed umbrella, and young boy seated, in blue suit). "Christmas" and poem beginning "Ah, in childish times," recto; "A" in "Ah" composed of tree branches.

Card 4 (girl in red dress holding a bouquet of flowers). "Christmas" and poem beginning "Past joys," recto; "P" in "Past" resembles illuminated initial.

Card 5 (two girls, one in blue polka-dot dress, the other in mustard color dress).

a. Poem beginning "On Christmas morning early," recto; "O" in "On" printed in gold.

b. Poem beginning "O New Year!," recto; "O" printed in gold.

Fine Art Society Invitation. 1891.

[4] p. Oblong. 12.7 x 17.4 cm.

"The honour of your Company is requested to view a Collec-

270. Envelope.

273. Invitation card.

tion of Drawings by Miss Kate Greenaway and Mr. Hugh Thomson on Saturday, 7th February, The Fine Art Society, 148. New Bond Street. _____ and Friend. 10 a.m. to 6 p.m.," p. [3].

Addressed to F. Locker Lampson, Esq.
Contains unsigned colored illustration by K.G., p. [1].
From the collection of Robert Partridge.
Presented by the Friends of the Detroit Public Library.

273.* Fine Art Society Invitation. 1898.
1 card. Oblong. 11.0 x 13.3 cm.
"Exhibition of Water Colours by Miss Kate Greenaway. The honour of your Company is requested at the Private View of the above on Saturday 19th February 1898, The Fine Art Society, 148 New Bond Street, 10 a.m. to 6 p.m. _____ and Friend.," and unsigned colored illustration by K.G., recto.
Addressed to J. Simpson Esq.
From the collection of Robert Partridge.
Presented by the Friends of the Detroit Public Library.

274. Fine Art Society Invitation. 1902.
1 card. Oblong. 13.6 x 16.2 cm.
"Exhibition of the Water Colour Drawings, &c left by the late Kate Greenaway. The Fine Art Society requests the honour of your Company at a Private View of the above, on Saturday, 11th January, 1902. 148 New Bond Street, London, 10 a.m. to 6 p.m. To admit two.," and colored illustration signed "K.G.," recto.
From the collection of Robert Partridge.
Presented by the Friends of the Detroit Public Library.

275. [Flowers & Fancies. London, Marcus Ward & Co.]
4 cards. 11.1 x 8.2 cm.
Greeting cards, printed in gold and colors, containing unsigned illustrations by K.G. from B. Montgomerie Ranking's *Flowers & Fancies*; 1.2-cm. decorative gold, blue, and yellow border, top and sides; 1.5-cm. gold, blue, yellow, and pink border, bottom.
Card 1. "Spring" (girl and boy with lamb). "Through the meadows we will stray / Where the lambkins are at play," recto; spring poem, verso.
Card 2. "Summer" (seated boy, girl standing with bouquet of flowers). "Flow'rets, flow'rets tell me pray. / Do I love him 'yea' or 'nay'?," recto; summer poem about flowers and love, verso.

*Illustrated.

146

Card 3. "Fall" (girl and boy seated in front of sheaves of wheat). "Among the cornsheaves lovers meet, / To read love legends sad and sweet," recto; fall poem, verso.

Card 4. "Winter" (winter scene of girl and boy under an umbrella). "The snow that all around we see / Is emblem of Love's purity," recto; winter poem, verso.

Titles for items 275–76 assigned by Means. (The illustrations for these cards were also used in *Calendar of the Seasons for 1876.*)

276. [Flowers & Fancies. London] Marcus Ward & Co.
    4 cards. 9.5 x 6.5 cm.
    Greeting cards printed in gold and colors, containing unsigned illustrations by K.G. from B. Montgomerie Ranking's *Flowers & Fancies;* 0.4-cm. scalloped edge.
    Card 1. "Spring" (girl and boy with lamb). "May Each Christmas Leave You Happier," recto.
    Card 2. "Summer" (seated boy, girl standing with bouquet of flowers). "A Happy New Year Be Before Thee," recto.
    Card 3. "Fall" (girl and boy seated in front of sheaves of wheat). "May Your Christmas Be As Happy," recto.
    Card 4. "Winter" (winter scene of girl and boy under an umbrella). "A Merry Christmas to You," recto.

277. [Going to the Party Set. London] Marcus Ward & Co.
    1 of 2 cards. Oblong. 10.1 x 16.0 cm.
    Greeting card, printed in colors, containing illustration signed "K.G."; 1.3-cm. border of holly and berries.
    Card 1. Going to the Party (procession of eight children in winter attire). "With Best Wishes," "Going to the Party," and song with music beginning "Overcoats and wrappers," recto; song continued, verso.
    Card 2. Dainty Airs. Missing.

278. [Going to the Party]
    1 card. Oblong. 9.0 x 16.0 cm.; two side flaps open in center to an overall size of 9.0 x 32.5 cm.
    Greeting card, printed in gold and colors on heavy card stock, containing unsigned illustration by K.G. On the outside is a floral design printed in gold, pink, and purple. On the inside is a procession of ten children in winter attire, center; poem on each inside flap; a 3-cm. bottom border contains a song with music, "Overcoats and wrappers, furs and muffatees, Hands deep down in pockets, cosy as you please. Little lads and lassies, Trotting through the snow, Tell us where you're going, We should like to know."

279. [Good Old Times. London] Marcus Ward & Co.
   2 of 3(?) cards. Oblong. 9.7 x 13.0 cm.
   Greeting cards, printed in colors, containing unsigned illustrations by K.G.; 1-cm. white border.
   Card 1 (two girls dancing). Ten-line poem beginning "In a dream I saw them stand," recto.
   Card 2 (girl in white with parasol, boy in green with crop). "With Best Wishes," and ten-line poem beginning "Good old times!," recto.
   Card 3 (girl in blue with pink parasol). Missing.

280. [Good Old Times. London] Marcus Ward & Co.
   2 of 3(?) cards. 12.4 x 9.5 cm.
   Greeting cards, printed in colors, containing unsigned illustrations by K.G.; 1.2-cm. white border.
   Card 1 (two girls dancing). Missing.
   Card 2 (girl in white, boy in green with crop). "To wish you a Happy New Year," recto.
   Card 3 (girl in blue with pink parasol). "With my best wishes for the season," recto.

281. [Goodall no. 501]
   1 of 4(?) cards. 10.5 x 8.9 cm.
   Greeting card, printed in colors on thick card stock, containing illustration signed "K.G."; beveled edges, gilt.
   Card 1. Ring-a-Ring of Roses.
   Cards 2–4. Missing.
   Although this card has the same illustration as the one in the Goodall series 501, it has no series statement.

282. Goodall No. 503. [London, Charles Goodall and Sons]
   4 cards. 11.8 x 9.2 cm.
   Greeting cards, printed in colors on thick card stock, containing illustrations signed "Kate Greenaway"; beveled edges, gilt; "The 'Kate Greenaway' Series No. 503. Goodall Trade Mare (*sic*)," verso.
   Card 1 (three girls in winter attire, holding open books). Four-line poem beginning "Friend-voices come from far away," recto.
   Card 2 (two girls seated at a table having tea). Six-line poem beginning "This is the way they take their teas," recto.
   Card 3 (five girls seated at a table eating a dinner). Ten-line poem beginning "I'd like to sit and sip my tea," recto.
   Card 4 (two standing girls, one in pink, the other in blue,

holding hands and closed fans). Four-line poem beginning "A Loving Pair," recto.

Presented by John S. Newberry.

283. Goodall No. 504. [London, Charles Goodall and Sons]
1 of 4 cards. Oblong. 8.4 x 18.5 cm.

Greeting card, printed in colors on thick card stock, containing signed illustration by K.G.; 1-cm. border; beveled edges, gilt.

Card 1 (six children in procession). "A Happy New Year" and two-line verse beginning "We children," recto; "The 'Kate Greenaway' Series No. 504, Goodall Trade Mare(*sic*)," verso.

Cards 2–4. Missing.

284. [Goodall No. 505]
2 of 4 cards. Oblong. 6.0 x 14.6 cm.

Greeting cards, white embossed Wedgwood style printed on paper stock, not mounted, containing signed illustrations by K.G.

Card 1 (seven women in procession). Printed on green background.

Card 2 (six children in procession).

a. Printed on green background.

b. Printed on tan background.

Cards 3 and 4. Missing.

Although these cards have the same illustrations and are in the same style as the Goodall series 505, they have no series statement.

285. Greenaway, Kate
Kate Greenaway's Calendar for 1884. London & New York, George Routledge & Sons.

4 cards. Oblong. 18.8 x 25.2 cm.

Cards are in a cream-colored envelope, with illustration by K.G. showing mother and two children in winter attire, printed in black; the little boy is holding a card which says "A Happy New Year to You" and the little girl is holding one which says "Christmas is Come."

Each card contains a calendar for 1884 and colored illustrations by K.G.

Presented by the Friends of the Detroit Public Library.

286. Greenaway, Kate
Kate Greenaway's Calendar for 1899.

149

1 card. Oblong. 18.7 x 25.0 cm.

Printed on heavy board.

"Engraved and Printed by Edmund Evans, Racquet Court, Fleet Street, E.C.," twelve colored illustrations by K.G. (one for each month) and the calendar for 1899, recto.

287. Greenaway, Kate

Kate Greenaway's Carols. London and New York, George Routledge & Sons.

4 cards. Oblong. 18.8 x 25.0 cm.

Cards are in a cream-colored envelope with title and illustration by K.G. of mother and two children in winter attire, printed in red; the little boy is holding a card which says "A Happy New Year to You" and the little girl is holding one which says "Christmas is Come."

Each card contains verses with colored illustrations by K.G.; one card includes music.

Two sets.

Presented by John S. Newberry.

288. Greenaway, Kate

[Grandmama's School Days] 1881.

Engraving. Black-and-white. 53.1 x 33.2 cm.

Signed "K. Greenaway" and "T. L. Atkinson" in pencil below engraving.

"London Published November 1st 1881 by Thomas McLean. 7. Haymarket. Copyright Registered.," recto.

Presented by John S. Newberry.

289. Greenaway, Kate

Kate Greenaway's Kalendar for 1897.

1 card. Oblong. 19.0 x 25.3 cm.

Printed on heavy board.

"Engraved and Printed by Edmund Evans, Racquet Court, Fleet Street, London, E.C.," four colored illustrations by K.G. and the calendar for 1897, recto.

290. Illustrated London News Advertisements for the Christmas Number, 1879.

5 cards. Oblong. 14.5 x 17.0 cm.

Each card contains a different unsigned colored illustration by K.G.

From the collection of Robert Partridge.

Presented by the Friends of the Detroit Public Library.

291. [Mother Goose . . . illustrated by Kate Greenaway]

Twelve trade cards containing unsigned illustrations by K.G. from *Mother Goose*.

Card 1. "Daffy-down-dilly." 10.4 x 6.6 cm. Printed in pink, tan, and white on gold background. "White, Black & Colors for Hand & Machine," four-line poem beginning "Where are you going my pretty maid" and J & P. Coats Best Six Cord 200 Yds 50," recto; advertisement for J & P. Coats, verso.

Card 2. "Jack Sprat." 10.1 x 6.1 cm. Printed in pink, white, and tan on gold background. "White, Black & Colors for Hand & Machine," "J & P. Coats Best Six Cord 200 Yds 50" and six-line poem beginning "Jack Sprat could eat no fat," recto; advertisement for J & P. Coats, verso.

Card 3. "Lucy Locket." 10.1 x 6.1 cm. Printed in shades of blue and white on gold background. "J & P. Coats Best Six Cord 200 Yds 50" and four-line poem beginning "Lucy Locket, lost her pocket," recto; advertisement for J & P. Coats, verso.

Card 4. "Cross Patch." 10.4 x 6.6 cm. Printed in pink, white, and tan on gold background. "White, Black & Colors for Hand & Machine," four-line poem beginning "Where are you going my pretty maid?," and "J & P. Coats Best Six Cord 200 Yds 50," recto. Advertisement for J & P. Coats, verso.

Card 5. "Jack and Jill." 10.3 x 6.6 cm. Printed in shades of blue and white on gold background. Six-line poem beginning "Jack and Jill" and "J & P. Coats Best Six Cord 200 Yds. 50," recto; advertisement for J & P. Coats, verso.

Card 6. "Polly." 10.1 x 6.6 cm. Printed in shades of blue and white on gold background. "J & P. Coats Best Six Cord 200 Yds. 50" and four-line poem beginning "Polly put the kettle on," recto; advertisement for J & P. Coats, verso.

Card 7. "Rock-a-bye Baby." 10.2 x 6.7 cm. Printed in shades of blue and white on gold background. "J & P. Coats Best Six Cord 200 Yds 50" and four-line poem beginning "Rock-a-bye Baby," recto; advertisement for J & P. Coats, verso.

Card 8. "See-Saw-Jack," 10.1 x 6.8 cm. Printed in pink, blue, and white on gold background. "White, Black & Colors for Hand & Machine," two-line poem beginning "See-saw-Jack in the Hedge" and "J & P. Coats Best Six Cord 200 Yds. 50," recto; advertisement for J & P. Coats, verso.

Card 9. "Little Maid." 10.2 x 6.7 cm. Printed in shades of blue and white on gold background. Four-line poem beginning "Little maid, little maid" and "J & P. Coats Best Six Cord 200 Yds. 50," recto; advertisement for J & P. Coats, verso.

Card 10. "My Mother." 10.1 x 6.6 cm. Printed in orange, blue, and white on gold background. "White, Black & Colors for Hand & Machine," "J & P. Coats Best Six Cord 200 Yds. 50," and four-line poem beginning "My mother and your mother," recto; advertisement for J & P. Coats, verso.

Card 11. "Tom, Tom." 10.1 x 6.7 cm. Printed in orange, brown, and white on gold background. "Metropolitan Mfg. Co.," "Buy the 'Eclipse,'" and four-line poem beginning "Tom, Tom, the piper's son," recto; advertisement for Metropolitan Manufacturing Co., verso.

Card 12. "Ring-a-ring of roses." 10.1 x 6.1 cm. Printed in pink, tan, and white on gold background. "White, Black & Colors for Hand & Machine," "J & P. Coats Best Six Cord 200 Yds. 50," and four-line poem beginning "Little ones may dance and play," recto; advertisement for J & P. Coats, verso.

292. [Page Boy Set. London] Marcus Ward & Co.
    4 cards. 13.0 x 9.0 cm.

    Greeting cards, printed in gold and colors, containing un-signed illustrations by K.G.; 1-cm. decorative gold and blue border.

    Card 1 (serving maid with envelope). "I send my serving maiden / with New Year letter laden," recto; poem beginning "I send the sweetest maid," verso.

    Card 2 (page in green at door knocker).

    a. "I've come this Christmas morn to know / if you've hung up the mistletoe," recto; poem beginning "Open the door—In haste am I," verso.

    b. "Here! ope the door and let me take / and give a kiss for Christmas sake," recto; poem beginning "Don't think me bold," verso.

    Card 3 (boy with plumed hat in hand). "My page's face can better say / than words my love on Christmas day," recto; poem beginning "A greeting by my page I send," verso.

    Card 4 (girl in ruffled hat with muff). "Will you not thank the little maiden / who comes with New Year wishes laden?," recto; poem beginning "I pray that in the fair New Year," verso.

    Title assigned by Means.

293. [Party Girl Set. London] Marcus Ward & Co.
    3 cards. 15.2 x 10.8 cm.

    Greeting cards, printed in colors, containing signed illus-trations by K.G.; 1.1-cm. blue and white border.

    Card 1 (girl with badminton racket).

    a. "Greeting," recto; "Thy own wish, wish I thee in every place," verso.

b. "Birthday," recto; "Wishing you every happiness and blessing," verso.

Card 2 (girl in rust-colored dress with beaver hat). "New Year," recto; "Wishing you every happiness and blessing," verso.

Card 3 (girl in green dress with bouquet of flowers and parasol). "Christmas," recto; "Thy own wish, wish I thee in every place!" verso.

Title assigned by Means.

294. [Procession Set. London] Marcus Ward & Co.
   2 cards. Oblong. 7.9 x 15.9 cm.
   Greeting cards, printed in colors, containing signed illustrations by K.G.; 1.4-cm. decorative border.
   Card 1 (procession, third figure from left facing right). Decorative border printed in blue and gold.
   a. "Well we love our roses sweet, yet we cast them at your feet; / and a garland we have twined, round about your life to wind," recto.
   b. "A garland fair for Christmas day your friend has sent and bade us say: / Of roses sweet may such a chain bind friend to friend thro' joy or pain," recto.
   Card 2 (procession, third figure from left facing left). Decorative border printed in gold and pink.
   a. Same verse as card 1*a* above.
   b. Same verse as card 1*b* above.

295. Programme April 13th 1898.
   1 card. 11.2 x 7.5 cm.
   Printed in brown and white. "Programme April 13th 1898" and illustration signed "K.G.," recto; list of dances, verso.

296. Reward of Merit Cards
   4 cards. 2 cards 4.7 x 6.7 cm.; 2 cards 6.7 x 4.7 cm.
   Reward of merit cards, printed in colors, containing unsigned illustrations by K.G. of children in winter attire; 0.2-cm. gold border. "Reward of Merit" printed on each card.

297. [Robin Hood and the Blackbird, a Tale of Christmas Dinner. London] Marcus Ward & Co.
   1 of 4 cards. Oblong. 9.0 x 14.4 cm.
   Greeting card, printed in colors, containing unsigned colored illustration attributed to K.G.; 1.4-cm. decorative green and tan border.
   Card 1 (five children in procession, one carrying a dead

blackbird). "If e'er you make a lucky hit / Be sure you make the best of it" and "A Happy New Year," recto; greeting dated "Dec. 25 '81," verso.

Cards 2–4. Missing.

298. Set of Eight XMas & New Year Cards By Kate Greenaway.

8 cards.

In original white envelope, with title printed in red.

Greeting cards, printed in colors, containing illustrations signed by K.G.

Card 1 (three girls seated, one holding a cat, and a boy holding a garland of flowers). 8.5 x 10.3 cm.

Card 2 (procession of seven children scattering flowers). 8.5 x 10.3 cm.

Card 3 (five children in a circle, holding a garland of yellow flowers). 9.0 x 10.5 cm.

Card 4 (five children in a circle, holding a garland of pink roses). 9.0 x 10.8 cm.

Cards 5–8 (same illustrations as "Goodall No. 503," without the verses). 13.3 x 9.4 cm.

Presented by the Friends of the Detroit Public Library.

299. Tile.

10.7 x 10.7 cm.

"Decorated by Deland Studio," verso.

Framed.

Contains colored illustration signed "K.G." on white background of four children dancing around sheaves of wheat, taken from *Kate Greenaway's Almanack for 1893,* August.

Presented by the Friends of the Detroit Public Library.

300. Tile.

15.3 x 15.3 cm.

"Minton Hollins & Co; Patent Tile Works. Stoke on Trent 2 R W," verso.

Contains unsigned colored illustration by K.G. on blue background of two girls perched on the branch of a tree, taken from *Marigold Garden,* p. 25.

Presented by John S. Newberry.

301. Transfer patterns.

2 sheets. 34.0 x 26.2 cm. (trimmed).

Each sheet contains six unsigned illustrations by K.G.

From the collection of Robert Partridge.

Presented by the Friends of the Detroit Public Library.

302. [Under the Window]

Trade cards, containing unsigned illustrations by K.G. from *Under the Window*.

Card 1 (back three-quarter view of girl sitting on a fence). Card in the shape of a fan.

  a. Printed in silver and pink.

  b. Printed in gold and pink; "Safford the Jeweler, 26 Wall St., Kingston, N.Y.," recto.

Card 2 (back three-quarter view of girl sitting on a fence). 11.8 x 6.3 cm. Printed in colors; 3-cm. bottom border for printing.

  a. "Compliments of Estes & Lauriat, Boston," recto; advertisement for the *Chatterbox* for 1880–'81, verso.

  b. "Easter cards... Chas. F. Ketcham, Stationer," recto; advertisement for Charles F. Ketcham, verso.

  c. "... Empire Knife Co.'s Cutlery... West Winsted, Conn.," recto; calling card for the Empire Knife Co. dated 1881, verso.

Card 3 (girl and boy sitting on a wall looking at snails). Card in the shape of a fan.

  a. Printed in blue and gold; "Imported Millinery M. Harrington... Palmer House, Chicago," recto.

  b. Printed in silver and pink; "From J. E. Kenfield's Ice Cream Parlor... Little Falls, N.Y.," recto.

Card 4 (girl in long dress and bonnet holding a bouquet of flowers). 11.8 x 6.3 cm. Printed in colors; 3-cm. bottom border for printing.

  a. "Compliments of Estes & Lauriat, Boston," recto; advertisement for The Carleton Series of Juveniles and *Our New Way 'Round the World*, verso.

  b. "... Berkshire Overall Co., Pittsfield, Mass.," recto.

Card 5 (side view of two girls carrying open umbrellas). 11.8 x 6.3 cm. Printed in colors; 3-cm. bottom border for printing.

  a. "Compliments of Estes & Lauriat, Boston," recto; advertisement for *Five Mice in a Mouse Trap* and *Babyhood*, verso.

  b. "Easter Cards... Chas. F. Ketcham, Stationer," recto; advertisement for Charles F. Ketcham, verso.

  c. "A Merry Christmas. A. J. Swain... Salem, Stationery, Books and Holiday Goods... ," recto; advertisement for The Carleton Series of Juveniles and *Our New Way 'Round the World*, verso.

Card 6 (two girls in winter attire with muffs). 11.8 x 6.3 cm. Printed in colors; 3-cm. bottom border for printing. "Compliments of Estes & Lauriat, Boston," recto; advertisement for *Five Mice in a Mouse Trap* and *Babyhood*, verso.

Card 7 (three girls in procession). 11.6 x 6.5 cm. Printed in colors; 2.8-cm. bottom border for printing. "Mr. Geo. W. Bar-

rett... Lewando's French Dye House... Boston, U.S.A.,"
recto; bottom border also contains small illustration by K.G.; list
of Lewando's fifteen departments, verso.

Card 8 (one girl standing at a table serving tea). 11.8 x 6.3 cm.
Printed in colors; 3-cm. bottom border for printing.

a. "Compliments of Estes & Lauriat, Boston," recto; advertisement for *Zigzag Journeys in Europe,* verso.

b. "Compliments of Johnson & Bailey, Dry Goods, Pittsfield,
Mass.," recto.

Card 9 (boy and girl fishing). 10.5 x 7.0 cm. Printed in blue and
gold. "Household Sewing Machine... Providence, R.I.," recto.

Card 10 (boy and girl dancing). 11.0 x 7.5 cm. Printed in blue
and gold. "Household Sewing Machine... Providence, R.I.,"
recto; announcement for the Manhattan Railway employees'
picnic, May 11, 1883, verso.

303. Wallpaper fragment.

2 fragments, 1 fragment 119.0 x 55.0 cm. (trimmed), 1 fragment 56.0 x 56.0 cm. (trimmed)

"Reproduced by Special Permission from Drawings by 'Kate
Greenaway.' Rd. No. 226515. 124," printed on the edge.

Contains colored illustrations for the months from *Kate
Greenaway's Almanack for 1893.*

From the collection of Robert Partridge.

Presented by the Friends of the Detroit Public Library.

304. Wallpaper fragment.

56.0 x 77.5 cm.

"Reproduced by Special Permission from Drawings by 'Kate
Greenaway.' Rd. No. 226521. 125," printed on the edge.

Contains colored illustrations for the seasons from *Kate
Greenaway's Almanack for 1893.*

From the collection of Robert Partridge.

Presented by the Friends of the Detroit Public Library.

305. Wood block.

8.9 x 8.9 cm.

"Kate Greenaway's Birthday Book for Children."

Wood block by Edmund Evans of cover design for *Kate
Greenaway's Birthday Book for Children,* containing title in the
center with illustrations by K.G. of the four seasons, one in each
corner.

From the collection of Robert Partridge.

Presented by the Friends of the Detroit Public Library.

ORIGINAL ART WORK, MANUSCRIPTS, AND LETTERS

The title of each item of art work is given where there is a title. Bracketed titles were supplied by the compiler. The date, if given on the item, follows the title. For other art work by K.G., see items 31*b*, 47*c*, 48*d*, 49*c*, 52*b*, 56*b*, 57*c*, 58*c*, 60*c*, 61*c*, 79*b*, 83*b*, and 108.

The date of each letter, the place from which it was written, the recipient and the place to which it was sent is given, followed by the number of pages and leaves and the dimensions. The height of the letter paper is noted. A brief description of the letter's contents is given. Again, information in brackets was supplied by the compiler. For other letters by K.G., see items 31*b* and 70.

306. [Almanack for 1890, July]
   Watercolor. 6.5 x 5.8 cm.
   Unsigned.
   "This is an original sketch by Kate Greenaway." Signed in holograph "John Greenaway," below drawing.
   Mounted at the beginning of M. H. Spielmann and G. S. Layard's *Kate Greenaway* (London, 1905), no. 8 of a deluxe edition of 500 copies.
   From the collection of Robert Partridge.
   Presented by the Friends of the Detroit Public Library.

307. [Almanack for 1894, June]
   Watercolor. 31.0 x 25.2 cm. Actual size of drawing 13.5 x 9.0 cm. Reduced upon publication to 7.3 x 5.0 cm.
   Signed "K.G."
   Matted and removed from frame. Frame has label from the Fine Art Society, London, pasted on back.
   Presented by the Friends of the Detroit Public Library.

308. [Almanack for 1894, July]
   Watercolor. 21.0 x 18.5 cm. Actual size of drawing 13.0 x 7.5 cm. Reduced upon publication to 7.5 x 4.5 cm.
   Signed "K.G."
   Matted and framed. Frame has label from the Fine Art Society, London, pasted on back.
   Presented by the Friends of the Detroit Public Library.

309. [Almanack for 1894, December]
   Watercolor. 21.0 x 17.2 cm. Actual size of drawing 12.5 x 9.5 cm. Reduced upon publication to 6.2 × 4.9 cm.
   Signed "K.G."
   Presented by the Friends of the Detroit Public Library.

310. [Back view of a woman in long dress and hat]
   Pencil sketch. 14.0 × 8.5 cm. Actual size of drawing 9.5 × 3.0 cm.
   Unsigned.
   From the estate of John Greenaway.
   Presented by the Friends of the Detroit Public Library.

311. [Kate Greenaway's Birthday Book for Children, January 14th]
   Pen-and-ink drawing. 3.2 x 2.3 cm. Reduced upon publication to 2.5 x 2.2 cm.
   Matted and framed with ten other pen-and-ink drawings from the *Birthday Book*.
   Presented by John S. Newberry.

312. [Kate Greenaway's Birthday Book for Children, January 30th]
   Pen-and-ink drawing. 2.6 x 1.6 cm.
   Matted and framed with ten other pen-and-ink drawings from the *Birthday Book*.
   Presented by John S. Newberry.

313. [Kate Greenaway's Birthday Book for Children, February 4th]
   Pen-and-ink drawing. 3.7 x 2.0 cm. Reduced upon publication to 2.6 x 1.4 cm.
   Matted and framed with ten other pen-and-ink drawings from the *Birthday Book*.
   Presented by John S. Newberry.

314. [Kate Greenaway's Birthday Book for Children, March 16th]
   Pen-and-ink drawing. 2.8 x 1.2 cm.
   Matted and framed with ten other pen-and-ink drawings from the *Birthday Book*.
   Presented by John S. Newberry.

315. [Kate Greenaway's Birthday Book for Children, March 21st]
   Pen-and-ink drawing. 3.3 x 2.4 cm. Reduced upon publication to 2.3 x 1.5 cm.
   Matted and framed with ten other pen-and-ink drawings from the *Birthday Book*.
   Presented by John S. Newberry.

316. [Kate Greenaway's Birthday Book for Children, April 4th]
Pen-and-ink drawing. 5.2 x 3.1 cm. Reduced upon publication to 2.5 x 1.5 cm.
Matted and framed with ten other pen-and-ink drawings from the *Birthday Book*.
Presented by John S. Newberry.

317. [Kate Greenaway's Birthday Book for Children, April 14th]
Pen-and-ink drawing. 2.7 x 2.9 cm.
Matted and framed with ten other pen-and-ink drawings from the *Birthday Book*.
Presented by John S. Newberry.

318. [Kate Greenaway's Birthday Book for Children, April 29th]
Pen-and-ink drawing. 3.4 x 2.9 cm. Reduced upon publication to 2.3 x 2.1 cm.
Matted and framed with ten other pen-and-ink drawings from the *Birthday Book*.
Presented by John S. Newberry.

319. [Kate Greenaway's Birthday Book for Children, April 30th]
Pen-and-ink drawing. 3.4 x 2.2 cm. Reduced upon publication to 2.5 x 1.5 cm.
Matted and framed with ten other pen-and-ink drawings from the *Birthday Book*.
Presented by John S. Newberry.

320. [Kate Greenaway's Birthday Book for Children, May 4th]
Pen-and-ink drawing. 3.0 x 2.6 cm.
Matted and framed with ten other pen-and-ink drawings from the *Birthday Book*.
Presented by John S. Newberry.

321. [Kate Greenaway's Birthday Book for Children, May 7th]
Pen-and-ink drawing. 3.3 x 2.1 cm. Reduced upon publication to 2.4 x 1.5 cm.
Matted and framed with ten other pen-and-ink drawings from the *Birthday Book*.
Presented by John S. Newberry.

322. [Bouquet of flowers in frame.]
Pencil sketch. 19.0 × 14.0 cm. Actual size of drawing 9.9 × 6.7 cm.
Unsigned.
From the estate of John Greenaway.
Presented by the Friends of the Detroit Public Library.

323. [Child in long white dress, green fur-trimmed coat, white muff, and white feathered hat, holding closed blue umbrella] 1899.
Watercolor. 14.8 × 10.5 cm. Actual size of drawing 7.4 × 4.0 cm.
Signed "K.G. 1899."
Presented by the Friends of the Detroit Public Library.

324. Child on balcony.
Pencil sketch. 19.5 x 14.4 cm. Actual size of drawing 5.5 x 3.0 cm.
Unsigned. Title in the hand of K.G.
From the estate of John Greenaway.
Presented by the Friends of the Detroit Public Library.

325. Dorothy A-1810-D
Watercolor. 13.0 x 8.5 cm.
Signed "K.G." Title in the hand of K.G.
Matted and framed.
Drawing of girl, possibly Dorothy Locker-Lampson, in 1810 costume: long green dress, blue-checked cape, and straw bonnet; she holds a bouquet of flowers in one hand and an open umbrella in the other.
Reproduced without umbrella to illustrate the month of June in *Calendar of the Months, 1884.*
Presented by John S. Newberry.

326. Every Girls Annual Illustrated.
Pencil sketch. 27.7 x 25.0 cm. Actual size of drawing 15.5 x 10.1 cm.
"Every Girls Annual Illustrated. Edited by Alicia A. Leith. Hatchards. Piccadily (*sic*). K.G.," in the hand of K.G.
Design for a title page.
Presented by John S. Newberry.

327. "George and the Chimney Sweeper."
Pencil sketch. 14.0 x 14.0 cm.
Unsigned. Title in the hand of K.G.
Drawing of four boys in front of a building, two of them with hoops; chimney sweeper in background.
"This is an original sketch by Kate Greenaway." Signed in holograph "John Greenaway," below drawing.
Mounted at the beginning of M. H. Spielmann and G. S. Layard's *Kate Greenaway* (London, 1905), no. 33 of deluxe edition of 500 copies.
Presented by John S. Newberry.

328.* [Girl in dress with bustle playing croquet with two small ladies and four gnomes; castle and trees in background]
  Pencil drawing. 21.7 x 27.3 cm.
  Unsigned.
  From the estate of John Greenaway.
  Presented by the Friends of the Detroit Public Library.

329. [Girl in long dress and hat, holding her skirt in one hand and walking; also a study of an arm]
  Pencil sketch. 9.0 x 12.2 cm.
  Unsigned.
  "This is an original sketch by Kate Greenaway." Signed in holograph "John Greenaway," below drawing.
  Mounted at the beginning of M. H. Spielmann and G. S. Layard's *Kate Greenaway* (London, 1905), no. 168 of deluxe edition of 500 copies.
  Presented by the Friends of the Detroit Public Library.

330. [Girl in long dress and hat, standing on her toes with her arms upstretched]
  Pencil sketch. 12.0 x 5.0 cm.
  Unsigned.
  "This is an original sketch by Kate Greenaway." Signed in holograph "John Greenaway," below drawing.
  Mounted at the beginning of M. H. Spielmann and G. S. Layard's *Kate Greenaway* (London, 1905), no. 120 of deluxe edition of 500 copies.
  Presented by the Friends of the Detroit Public Library.

331.* [Girl in long dress, gray and pink cape and hat, holding a muff]
  Watercolor. 34.5 x 23.0 cm.
  Signed "K.G."
  Matted and framed. Frame has label from the Fine Art Society, London, pasted on back.
  Presented by the Friends of the Detroit Public Library.

332. [Girl in long dress with short curly hair, holding a doll]
  Pencil sketch. 8.0 x 5.5 cm.
  Unsigned.
  "This is an original sketch by Kate Greenaway." Signed in holograph "John Greenaway," below drawing.
  Mounted at the beginning of M. H. Spielmann and G. S.

*Illustrated.

Layard's *Kate Greenaway* (London, 1905), no. 489 of deluxe edition of 500 copies.

Presented by the Friends of the Detroit Public Library.

333. [Girl in long green fur-trimmed coat, muff, and feathered hat] Dec. 31, 1896.

Watercolor and pencil. 13.0 x 7.6 cm. Actual size of drawing 6.5 x 4.5 cm.

Signed "K.G. Dec. 31, 1896 to Mrs. Samuel."

Framed.

Presented by John S. Newberry.

334.* [Girl in winter attire: long red dress, pink ribboned hat, fur-trimmed cape, and muff]

Chalk drawing. 32.8 x 24.4 cm.

Unsigned.

Presented by John S. Newberry.

335.* The Green Wave.

Watercolor. 19.7 x 13.8 cm. Actual size of drawing 6.4 x 12.5 cm.

Unsigned. Title in the hand of K.G.

Matted.

Drawing of a young woman in long white dress lying on the shore; waves and four water sprites dancing in background; twenty-four-line poem in the hand of K.G. above and below drawing.

Presented by the Friends of the Detroit Public Library.

336.* He really *has* come at last. October 1, 1884.

Watercolor and pencil. Oblong 16.8 x 25.4 cm.

Signed "K.G. October 1st 1884." Title in the hand of K.G.

Drawing of six girls in long dresses with pink and blue sashes; one girl is rushing towards the other five, waving a handkerchief. The style of the dresses, size, and date of this drawing seem to indicate a relationship to item 358.

Presented by the Friends of the Detroit Public Library.

337. [Head of a young boy, wearing a brown hat]

Watercolor. 4.0 x 4.0 cm.

Unsigned.

"This is an original sketch by Kate Greenaway." Signed in holograph "John Greenaway," below drawing.

*Illustrated.

328. Pencil drawing. 21.7 x 27.3 cm.

Mounted at the beginning of M. H. Spielmann and G. S. Layard's *Kate Greenaway* (London, 1905), no. 8 of deluxe edition of 500 copies.

From the collection of Robert Partridge.

Presented by the Friends of the Detroit Public Library.

338.* [Hetty and Mina]

10 items.

Unsigned.

From the estate of John Greenaway.

Presented by the Friends of the Detroit Public Library.

1. Two girls sitting under a tree looking at a miniature-sized girl; a fish is looking on.

Pen-and-ink and pencil drawing. 15.2 x 12.4 cm. Matted on gray paper, 23.7 x 19.0 cm.

"Hetty and Mina . . Listening to the tale of the Little Shepheardess (*sic*) . . ," in the hand of K.G., written on mat below drawing.

2. Two girls holding up their skirts as they wade through water following a fish.

Pen-and-ink and pencil drawing. 14.0 x 11.1 cm. Matted on gray paper, 23.7 x 19.0 cm.

"So . . they walked . . down the river . . the Little Fish . . swimming on before them," in the hand of K.G., written on mat below drawing.

3. Two girls walking through a forest with surprised expressions as they see a donkey, a frog, and a broom with a face on it.

Pen-and-ink and pencil drawing. 16.0 x 12.3 cm. Matted on gray paper, 23.7 x 19.0 cm.

"The . . first found Inhabitants," in the hand of K.G., written on mat below drawing.

4. Two girls, one of them holding a broom with a face on it, and the fish standing, talking to a little person with a chubby face with brushes for arms and wooden legs; a personified scissors; a thimble and thread in foreground, umbrella tree in background.

Pen-and-ink and pencil drawing. 15.7 x 11.8 cm. Matted on gray paper, 23.7 x 19.0 cm.

"Punch's . . distant relations," in the hand of K.G., written on mat below drawing.

5. Girl holding broom with face on it, looking at a row of jack-in-the-boxes; kneeling fish in foreground; straw person and tree with faces on its fruit in background.

*Illustrated.

166

338 1. Pen-and-ink and pencil drawing. 15.2 x 12.4 cm. "Hetty and Mina . . Listening to the tale of the Little Shepheardess . . ," in the hand of K.G., written on the mat below drawing.

338 2. Pen-and-ink and pencil drawing. 14.0 x 11.1 cm. "So . . they walked . . down the river . . the Little Fish . . swimming on before them," in the hand of K.G., written on the mat below drawing.

Pen-and-ink and pencil drawing. 16.6 x 12.2 cm. Matted on gray paper, 23.7 x 19.0 cm.

"The Conservatory . . in funny country," in the hand of K.G., written on mat below drawing.

6. Two girls surrounded by a crowd of little people; three of the little people, in elf-like costume, standing on stools, are blowing bubbles at one of the girls.

Pen-and-ink and pencil drawing. 13.9 x 11.4 cm. Matted on gray paper, 23.7 x 19.0 cm.

"Mina . . receives punishment at the hands of the Angry Man . . ," in the hand of K.G., written on mat below drawing.

7. Girl riding a large cat surrounded by a bird flying on a broom, an elf, and flowers with faces.

Pen-and-ink and pencil drawing. 14.5 x 10.5 cm. Matted on gray paper, 23.7 x 19.0 cm.

"Mina's Strange ride," in the hand of K.G., written on mat below drawing.

8. Girl kneeling next to a pole holding up a stuffed figure, broom with face throwing sticks at pole.

Pen-and-ink and pencil drawing. 14.9 x 11.6 cm. Matted on gray paper, 23.7 x 19.0 cm.

"The way to speak to Griffin Gruffen," in the hand of K.G., written on mat below drawing.

9. Two girls, one holding a broom with a face on it, with fish standing at their side; a little duke and duchess in front of them looking at a caped figure; several little people in background.

Pen-and-ink and pencil drawing. 15.5 x 12.2 cm. Matted on gray paper, 23.7 x 19.0 cm.

"Then . . Manage . . your Affairs by yourself Said the little duchess," in the hand of K.G., written on mat below drawing.

10. Two girls watching a race of little people riding ducks, some smiling and some crying; windmills in the background.

Pen-and-ink and pencil drawing. 17.5 x 13.7 cm. Matted on gray paper, 23.7 x 19.0 cm.

"The . . race between the laughs . . and the crys.," in the hand of K.G., written on mat below drawing.

These ten drawings are on blue paper, the same as in K.G.'s *Sketchbook*, 1868. Since the *Sketchbook* has some pages cut out, and one of the drawings in the *Sketchbook* contains the same girl and a broom with a face, it is very possible that at least some of these drawings might be the missing pages.

339. Letter, n.d., Hampstead, to [A. W.] Tuer, n.p.
    1 p. 15.5 cm.
    Holograph signed.

338 4. Pen-and-ink and pencil drawing. 15.7 x 11.8 cm. "Punch's . . distant relations," in the hand of K.G., written on the mat below drawing.

338 3. Pen-and-ink and pencil drawing. 16.0 x 12.3 cm. "The . . first found Inhabitants," in the hand of K.G., written on the mat below drawing.

K.G. thanks Tuer for "all the trouble you have taken—I hope they will not find their way into London again."
Presented by John S. Newberry.

340. Letter, n.d., n.p., to [Edmund] Evans, n.p.
[4] p. on 1 folded l. 15.5 cm.
Holograph signed.
K.G. complains that she has seen some of her work "shamefully adapted and altered"; she will send the complete alphabet tomorrow—"that will be the end of the book"—and asks if he wants to do *Marigold Garden* next: "I have some of the sketches done for Marigold Garden—it has as much chance as any I should think."
Presented by the Friends of the Detroit Public Library.

341. Letter, July 3, 1882, Holloway, to Miss Field, n.p.
[2] p. on 1 l. 15.2 cm.
Holograph signed.
K.G. declines an invitation because she is too busy with her work.
Presented by Mr. and Mrs. Glenn M. Coulter.

342. Letter, April 29, 1885, Hampstead, to [R. Norman] Shaw, n.p.
[2½] p. on 1 folded l. 15.5 cm.
Holograph signed.
K.G., writing to the architect who designed her house at 39, Frognal, Hampstead, describes it as a "comfort" and a "Paradise," and says that she doesn't know how she'll ever thank him enough.
Presented by the Friends of the Detroit Public Library.

343. Letter, June 9, 1885, Hampstead, to A. W. Tuer, n.p.
[2] p. on 1 l. 15.5 cm.
Holograph signed.
K.G. arranges an appointment with Tuer on either Wednesday or Saturday.
Presented by John S. Newberry.

344. Letter, July 18, 1887, Hampstead, to Miss Jeaffreson, n.p.
[4] p. on 1 folded l. 15.3 cm.
Holograph signed.
K.G. explains that she has not been well and must take a "long rest and holiday," and graciously declines to illustrate Miss Jeaffreson's little book.
Presented by the Friends of the Detroit Public Library.

338 6. Pen-and-ink and pencil drawing. 13.9 x 11.4 cm. "Mina . . receives punishment at the hands of the angry man . . ," in the hand of K.G., written on the mat below drawing.

338 5. Pen-and-ink and pencil drawing. 16.6 x 12.2 cm. "The Conservatory . . in funny country," in the hand of K.G., written on the mat below drawing.

345. Letter, July 24, 1891, Hampstead, to Bertha, n.p.
    1 p. 15.5 cm.
    Holograph signed, on mourning stationery.
    K.G. tells Bertha to "*Do come*—it's too good of you to spend so much of your time on me."
    Presented by Mr. & Mrs. Glenn M. Coulter.

346.* Letter, December 5, 1891, Hampstead, to Miss Durham, n.p.
    1 p. 15.5 cm.
    Holograph signed.
    K.G. sends her autograph. The note is surrounded by seven pen-and-ink drawings by K.G., five of them of heads, one of a flower, and one of a small child pulling a cart.
    Presented by John S. Newberry.

347. Letter, July 27, 1892, Hampstead, to Gleeson White, n.p.
    1 p. 15.3 cm.
    Holograph signed.
    K.G. tells White she has only designed two bookplates, one for Mr. Locker-Lampson and one for his son, Godfrey Locker-Lampson.
    Presented by the Friends of the Detroit Public Library.

348. Letter, October 16, 1894, Hampstead, to Lady Maria [Ponsonby], n.p.
    [4] p. on 1 folded l. 15.5 cm.
    Holograph signed, on mourning stationery.
    K.G. discusses her new housemaid, shopping in the London shops, and the Ponsonby's new house. She states: "Tell Mr. Ponsonby *I hate* Beardsley more than ever." In the second part of the letter, dated October 21, K.G. discusses portrait exhibitions and her enjoyment of summer.
    Presented by the Friends of the Detroit Public Library.

349. Letter, November 23, 1896, Hampstead, to Mrs. Paget, n.p.
    [3] p. on 1 folded l. 15 cm.
    Holograph signed.
    K.G. returns Mrs. Paget's little books, sends her this year's *Almanack,* and invites her to "have tea in my studio."
    Presented by Charles E. Feinberg in memory of John S. Newberry.

350. Letter, May 3, 1898, Hampstead, to Lady Jeune, n.p.
    [3] p. on 1 folded l. 15.3 cm.

*Illustrated.

172

338 8. Pen-and-ink and pencil drawing. 14.9 x 11.6 cm. "The way to speak to Griffin Gruffen," in the hand of K.G., written on the mat below drawing.

338 7. Pen-and-ink and pencil drawing. 14.5 x 10.5 cm. "Mina's Strange ride," in the hand of K.G., written on the mat below drawing.

Holograph signed.

K.G. asks to come and pick up the book, and comments: "I wish there could be two springs then there would be time to try to Paint them."

Presented by the Friends of the Detroit Public Library.

351. Letter, August 3, 1898, Hampstead, to Lady Tennyson, n.p.
     1 p. 15.3 cm.
     Holograph signed.
     K.G. accepts an invitation to pay a visit from the 12th to the 15th.
     Presented by the Friends of the Detroit Public Library.

352. Letter, January 22, 1900, Hampstead, to [Marion Harry] Spielmann, n.p.
     [4] p. on 1 folded l. 15.3 cm.
     Holograph signed.
     K.G. explains why she will not send to the Paris Exhibition, expresses her sadness over the death of Mr. Ruskin, talks about a bookplate, and says that she will give Mr. Spielmann "the dates of the Books as well as I can, I know how they each come but not the exact date at which they were published."
     Presented by the Friends of the Detroit Public Library.

353. Letter, June 6, 1901, Hampstead, to Lady Dorothy [Nevill], n.p.
     [3] p. on 1 folded l. 15.0 cm.
     Holograph signed.
     K.G. expresses her pleasure at seeing Lady Dorothy and giving her some drawings.
     Presented by the Friends of the Detroit Public Library.

354. Letter, June 7, 1901, Hampstead, to Lady Flower, London.
     [3] p. on 1 folded l. 15.0 cm.
     Holograph signed, with envelope.
     K.G. regrets that she has not written sooner but has "been so ill the past year that I have been able to do so little."
     Presented by the Friends of the Detroit Public Library.

355. [Little boy seated, holding a ball]
     Pencil sketch. 19.0 x 14.0 cm. Actual size of drawing 4.0 x 4.3 cm.
     Unsigned. "There was a little boy whose name was Harry," written in pencil below the drawing in the hand of K.G.
     From the estate of John Greenaway.
     Presented by the Friends of the Detroit Public Library.

338 10. Pen-and-ink and pencil drawing. 17.5 x 13.7 cm. "The race between the laughs . . and the crys . . ," in the hand of K.G., written on the mat below drawing.

338 9. Pen-and-ink and pencil drawing. 15.5 x 12.2 cm. "Then . . Manage . . your Affairs by yourself Said the little duchess," in the hand of K.G., written on the mat below drawing.

356. [Mother and child]
Watercolor. 17.5 x 14.5 cm.
Signed "K.G."
Woman seated on a pillow holding the hands of a little girl who is dancing.
Presented by John S. Newberry.

357. [Mother and child] October 1, 1887.
Watercolor. 20.2 x 16.3 cm. Actual size of drawing 9.5 x 13.0 cm.
Signed "Kate Greenaway 1st October 1887."
Matted and framed.
Drawing of mother carrying a basket of roses and little girl with roses gathered in her apron, walking in a meadow.
Presented by John S. Newberry.

358.* [Procession] October 1, 1884.
Watercolor and pencil. 16.5 x 28.8 cm.
Signed "K.G. 1st October 1884."
Drawing of procession of girls in long dresses with pink and blue sashes carrying a cake, a cart with a large teacup, toasting forks, and bouquets. The style of the dresses, size, and date of this drawing seem to indicate a relationship to item 336.
Presented by John S. Newberry.

359. Programme. April 13th, 1898.
Pen-and-ink drawing. 18.5 x 12.6 cm. Actual size, including words and drawing of a girl seated next to a spinning wheel, 10.3 x 6.3 cm.
Signed "K.G."
Presented by the Friends of the Detroit Public Library.

360.* [Self-portrait] 1883.
Watercolor. 14.5 x 10.8 cm.
Signed "Yours K.G. 1883."
Drawing of a side view of K.G. in black hat with pompoms and beige cape.
Presented by John S. Newberry.

361. [Side view of two girls, one in long coat, bonnet, and muff, the other unfinished]
Pencil sketch. 8.0 x 8.0 cm.
Unsigned.

*Illustrated.

176

5.th December 1891

50, FROGNAL,
HAMPSTEAD. N.W.

Dear Miss Durham

I Have great Pleasure in
sending you my Autograph
as you were good enough to
wish to Have it

Yours Truly
Kate Greenaway

346. K.G. sends her autograph.

177

"This is an original sketch by Kate Greenaway." Signed in holograph "John Greenaway," below drawing.

Mounted at the beginning of M. H. Spielmann and G. S. Layard's *Kate Greenaway* (London, 1905), no. 128 of deluxe edition of 500 copies.

Presented by the Friends of the Detroit Public Library.

362.* [Sketchbook] 1868.

[64] l. Blue paper. 22.6 cm.

Marbled boards. Leather spine and corners. Marbled endpapers.

Decorative printed title page signed "Kate Greenaway 1868," l. [1] recto.

Contains 76 pages of pencil, pen-and-ink, and wash drawings and sketches, many of them occupying the full page. The sketches on leaves [54] recto and [57] recto are for the illustrations "The Princess Dancing" and "Nonsense about Cat's-Cradle," published in *People's Magazine* in 1873.

Leaves [23, 27, 28, 31, 33, 34, and 51] have been cut out. It is possible that the drawings for "Hetty and Mina" (item 338) might be some of the missing pages.

Presented by John S. Newberry.

363. The Spring bringing in the Season. Dec. 31, 1884.

Watercolor and pencil. 20.5 x 25.2 cm.

Signed "K.G. New Years Eve. 1884."

Title in the hand of K.G.

Drawing of a procession of five young women in long dresses with pink, blue, and green sashes, carrying garlands of flowers and fruit.

Presented by John S. Newberry.

364. [Three little boys, one seated and crying]

Pencil sketch. 19.1 x 14.0 cm. Actual size of drawing 6.0 x 5.5 cm.

Unsigned.

"One day in the month of June, Thomas had got all his things ready to set out on a Little jaunt of pleasure," written below the drawing in the hand of K.G.

From the estate of John Greenaway.

Presented by the Friends of the Detroit Public Library.

*Illustrated.

362. Pen-and-ink, pencil, and wash drawing. 22.6 x 18.1 cm. From K.G.'s *Sketchbook*, 1868.

362. Pen-and-ink and pencil drawing. 22.6 x 18.1 cm. From K.G.'s *Sketchbook*, 1868.

362. Pen-and-ink and pencil drawing. 13.0 x 18.1 cm. From K.G.'s *Sketchbook*, 1868.

362. Pen-and-ink and pencil drawing. 13.7 x 18.1 cm. From K.G.'s *Sketchbook*, 1868.

362. Pen-and-ink and pencil drawing. 22.6 x 18.1 cm.
From K.G.'s *Sketchbook*, 1868.

362. Pen-and-ink and pencil drawing. 14.0 x 13.0 cm.
From K.G.'s *Sketchbook*, 1868.

362. Pen-and-ink and pencil drawing. 16.2 x 11.5 cm. From K.G.'s *Sketchbook*, 1868.

362. Pen-and-ink, pencil, and wash drawing. 16.0 cm. in diameter. From K.G.'s *Sketchbook*, 1868.

362. Pen-and-ink drawing. 11.7 x 8.5 cm. From K.G.'s *Sketchbook*, 1868.

362. Pen-and-ink and pencil drawing. 16.0 x 9.6 cm.
From K.G.'s *Sketchbook*, 1868.

362. Pen-and-ink and pencil drawing. 12.5 x 8.0 cm.
From K.G.'s *Sketchbook*, 1868.

362. Pencil and wash drawing. 15.3 x 10.2 cm. From K.G.'s *Sketchbook*, 1868.

362. Pencil drawing. 12.9 x 8.3 cm. From K.G.'s *Sketchbook*, 1868.

365. [Woman with shovel in hand and child]
Pencil sketch. 9.2 x 9.2 cm.
Unsigned.
"This is an original sketch by Kate Greenaway." Signed in holograph "John Greenaway," below drawing.
Mounted at the beginning of M. H. Spielmann and G. S. Layard's *Kate Greenaway* (London, 1905), unnumbered copy of deluxe edition of 500 copies.
From the collection of Robert Partridge.
Presented by the Friends of the Detroit Public Library.

AWARDS

366. Duppa, R., and Quatremère De Quincy

    The Lives and Works of Michael Angelo and Raphael. London: H. G. Bohn, 1861

    "Science and Art Department of the Committee of Council on Education. Finsbury School of Art. Presented to Catherine Greenaway instead of a Local Medal, for success in Stage 22a of the Course of Instruction in Art. By Order of the Lords of the Committee of Privy Council on Education. MDCCCLXIV.," printed bookplate on inside front cover. "Finsbury," "Catherine Greenaway," and "22a" written in an unknown hand.

    From the estate of John Greenaway.

    Presented by the Friends of the Detroit Public Library.

367. Gullick, Thomas John, and John Timbs

    Painting Popularly Explained. London: Kent and Co., 1859

    "Science and Art Department of the Committee of Council on Education. Finsbury School of Art. Presented to Catherine Greenaway instead of a Local Medal, for success in Stage 4.b. of the Course of Instruction in Art. By Order of the Lords of the Committee of Privy Council on Education. MDCCCLXII.," printed bookplate on inside front cover. "Finsbury," "Catherine Greenaway," and "4.b." written in an unknown hand.

    From the estate of John Greenaway.

    Presented by the Friends of the Detroit Public Library.

368. Copper medallion

    14.0 x 14.0 cm.

    "Victoria Queen by the Grace of God 1857" in center. "For success in the National Art Competition" at bottom. "Catherine Greenaway 1864. Stage XXII" engraved in oval shield.

    Medallion enclosed in a wooden case with "V R Science and Art Department" stamped in gold on top cover.

    Accompanied by "Description of the National Medallion. Executed in Repoussé by M. Vechte." [1] l. 14.9 x 14.9 cm.

    "The Medallion is awarded in the yearly National Competition of the Students of all the Art-Schools of the United Kingdom and is the highest prize for the success in art given by the

Science and Art Department of the Committee of Council on Education," recto.

From the estate of John Greenaway.

Presented by the Friends of the Detroit Public Library.

369. Tennyson, Alfred

Idylls of the King. London: Edward Moxon & Co., 1864

"This book was awarded to Miss C. Greenaway, as a prize, by the members of the Sketching Class, for having had the greatest number of sketches selected & marked 'The Best' by Mr. Denby during the sketching session, ending Feb. 1865" written in an unknown hand, recto front flyleaf.

From the estate of John Greenaway.

Presented by the Friends of the Detroit Public Library.

370. Timbs, John

Anecdote Biography. London: Richard Bentley, 1860

"Science and Art Department of the Committee of Council on Education. Finsbury School of Art. Presented to Catherine Greenaway instead of a Local Medal, for success in Stage 1/ob 22c of the Course of Instruction in Art. By Order of the Lords of the Committee of Privy Council on Education. MDCCCLXIII.," printed bookplate on inside front cover. "Finsbury," "Catherine Greenaway," and "1/ob 22c" written in an unknown hand.

From the estate of John Greenaway.

Presented by the Friends of the Detroit Public Library.

SELECTED
BIBLIOGRAPHY
from the Collection

The following items have been selected for inclusion here because of their research value.

371. Buday, George
    The History of the Christmas Card. London: Rockliff, [1954].

372. Castle, Egerton
    English Book-Plates, Ancient and Modern. London: G. Bell, 1894.

373. Detroit Public Library
    The John S. Newberry Gift Collection of Kate Greenaway Presented to the Detroit Public Library. Frances J. Brewer, comp. Detroit: Friends of the Detroit Public Library, 1959.

374. Dobson, Austin
    "Art in the Nursery." *Magazine of Art*, February 1883, pp. 127–32.

375. Dobson, Austin
    De Libris; Prose & Verse. London: Macmillan and Co., 1908.

376. Doheny, Mrs. Edward L.
    A Collection of Kate Greenaway Belonging to Mrs. Edward L. Doheny. Ellen Shaffer, comp. Los Angeles, Calif.: Dawson's Book Shop, 1942.

377. Evans, Edmund
    The Reminiscences of Edmund Evans. Oxford: Clarendon Press, 1967.

378. Fine Art Society, London
    Catalogue of a Collection of Drawings by Miss Kate Greenaway and Hugh Thomson. Exhibited at the Fine Art Society. Preface by Lionel Robinson. London: Fine Art Society, 1891.

379. Greenaway, Kate
    The Kate Greenaway Treasury; an Anthology of the Illus-

trations and Writings of Kate Greenaway. Edward Ernest, ed., with Patricia Tracy Lowe. Introduction by Ruth Hill Viguers. Cleveland: World Publishing Co., c. 1967.

380. Greenaway, Kate
   Sixteen Examples in Colour of the Artist's Work. Introduction by M. H. Spielmann. London: A. & C. Black, 1910.

381. Labouchere, Norma
   Ladies' Book-Plates, an Illustrated Handbook for Collectors and Book-Lovers. London: G. Bell, 1894.

382. Meacham, M. I.
   The Kate Greenaway Collection of Miss M. I. Meacham of New York City.... To be Sold by Her Order Monday Afternoon, December 12 at Two-Thirty o'Clock. New York: Anderson Galleries, 1921.

383. Means, Carroll Alton
   "Kate Greenaway's Valentines. Part I." *Hobbies* 57 (February 1953): 20–21, 64.

384. Means, Carroll Alton
   "Kate Greenaway's Valentines. Part II." *Hobbies 58 (March 1953): 20–21, 66.*

385. Means, Carroll Alton
   "Kate Greenaway's Valentines. Part III." *Hobbies* 58 (April 1953): 24–25, 79.

386. Means, Carroll Alton
   "Kate Greenaway's Valentines. Part IV." *Hobbies* 58 (May 1953): 38–39.

387. Means, Carroll Alton
   "Kate Greenaway's Valentines. Part V." *Hobbies* 58 (June 1953): 38–39, 43.

388. Means, Carroll Alton
   "Kate Greenaway's Valentines. Part VI." *Hobbies* 58 (July 1953): 42–43, 47.

389. Moore, Annie Carroll
   A Century of Kate Greenaway. New York: F. Warne, [1946].

390. Newcomb, Covelle
     The Secret Door; the Story of Kate Greenaway. New York:
     Dodd, Mead, c. 1946.

391. Partridge, Robert
     Manuscript notebook arranged alphabetically containing Kate
     Greenaway items. n.d.

392. Phillips, Sons & Neale, auctioneers, London
     Books Also Maps and Manuscripts; Also a Collection of Chil-
     dren's Books Including Original Drawings by Kate
     Greenaway . . . To Be Sold by Auction on Tuesday, January 25,
     1972. London: Phillips, Sons & Neale, 1972.

393. Phillips, Sons & Neale, auctioneers, London
     Water Colours, Drawings and Books, etc. by Kate Green-
     away. . . . To Be Sold by Auction on Tuesday, November 16,
     1971. London: Phillips, Sons & Neale, 1971.

394. Rumbold, John
     "Kate Greenaway's First Christmas Card. Part I." *Hobbies* 61
     (December 1956): 56–57, 60.

395. Rumbold, John
     "Kate Greenaway's First Christmas Card. Part II." *Hobbies* 61
     (January 1957): 57–59.

396. Sasscier, Agnes L.
     "Greenaway Christmas Cards." *Hobbies* 55 (December 1950):
     16–17, 40, 84–85.

397. Sotheby, auctioneers, London
     Art at Auction 1970/71. London: Sotheby, 1971.
     Contains "Kate Greenaway, her Books and Drawings," by
     Michael Heseltine, pp. 209–17.

398. Sotheby, auctioneers, London
     Catalogue of Valuable Books, Manuscripts, Autographs, Let-
     ters, Etc. . . . The Lewis Carroll and Kate Greenaway Collections
     the Property of the Comte de Suzannet. London: Sotheby, 1935.

399. Spielmann, Marion Harry
     Correspondence, 1904–1943.
     ca. 90 items.

Correspondence with M. H. Spielmann, mainly relating to the publication of *Kate Greenaway* (London: A. & C. Black, 1905). Includes letters from A. & C. Black, Violet Dickinson, Austin Dobson, John Greenaway, Lady Victoria Herbert, G. S. Layard, Jane Locker-Lampson, Maud Locker-Lampson, and James B. Pinker.

From the collection of Robert Partridge.

Presented by the Friends of the Detroit Public Library.

400. Spielmann, Marion Harry, and G. S. Layard
Kate Greenaway. London: A. and C. Black, 1905.
Includes prospectus and order form.

401. Stutz, Caroline A., and Ethel McPhail
"Kate Greenaway and Her Influence on Related Arts. *National Button Bulletin* 8, no. 6 (1949): 362–83.

402. Tarbox, Alice T.
The Magic Land of Kate Greenaway. Southington, Conn.: Just Buttons, 1968.

ADDENDA

The following items were added to the collection after this catalogue had been completed.

403.   A BOOK | FOR | EVERY LITTLE | JACK AND GILL. | ILLUS-
       TRATED. | NEW YORK: | DODD, MEAD & COMPANY | PUB-
       LISHERS.

       [5] 8–46 p. 22.5 cm.

       Glazed pictorial boards. *Front cover:* A BOOK FOR EVERY
       JACK AND GILL | DODD , MEAD & CO., NEW YORK, printed
       in black; picture of seated boy and girl reading a book, printed in
       colors. *Spine:* dark green cloth. *Back cover:* floral design, printed
       in brown and white. Cream-colored endpapers.

       "Copyright 1879, by Dodd, Mead & Company.," p. [4] (verso
       of title page).

       Contains a black-and-white illustration signed "K.G.," p. 22.

       Presented by Mr. and Mrs. Joseph Barta, Mr. and Mrs.
       William Vance, and Mr. and Mrs. George Garner in memory of
       Bernadine Baker.

404.   Ewing, Juliana Horatia
       BROTHERS | OF | PITY | AND OTHER TALES OF | BEASTS
       AND MEN | BY | JULIANA HORATIA EWING | AUTHOR OF
       "JACKANAPES," "OLD FASHIONED FAIRY TALES," &c. &c.
       | EIGHTH THOUSAND. | PUBLISHED UNDER THE DIREC-
       TION OF | THE COMMITTEE OF GENERAL LITERATURE
       AND EDUCATION | APPOINTED BY THE SOCIETY FOR
       PROMOTING | CHRISTIAN KNOWLEDGE | LONDON: | Soci-
       ety for Promoting Christian Knowledge, | NORTHUMBER-
       LAND AVENUE, CHARING CROSS, S.W. | 43, QUEEN
       VICTORIA STREET, E.C.; | 26, ST. GEORGE'S PLACE, HYDE
       PARK CORNER, S.W. | BRIGHTON: 135, NORTH STREET. |
       NEW YORK: E. & J. B. YOUNG & CO. | 1884.

       [ix] x [xi–xii] [1] 2–199 [200] [1] 2–12 p. 18.0 cm.

       Gray cloth. *Front cover:* BROTHERS | of PITY | & | Other
       TALES OF | BEASTS & MEN: | BY J. H. EWING:, stamped in
       gold and black; picture of two beetles digging with shovels and
       an ivy design with owl's head, stamped in black and gold. *Spine:*
       BROTHERS | of | PITY: | & | Other | Tales: | J. H. EWING:,

stamped in black and gold; with head of a rooster, ivy leaf, and publisher's monogram, stamped in black. *Back cover:* dog, flowers, and fox, stamped in black and gold. Gray and white floral endpapers. Thickness of volume excluding covers: 1.5 cm.

"Ballantyne Press, Ballantyne, Hanson and Co., Edinburgh, Chandos Street, London," p. [ii].

"Books by the same author," p. [200].

"Publications of the Society for Promoting Christian Knowledge," pp. [1] 2–12 at end.

"Depositories. London: Northumberland Avenue, Charing Cross. S.W.: 43, Queen Victoria Street, E.C.; 26 St. George's Place, Hyde Park Corner, S.W. Brighton: 135 North Street," p. 12 at end.

Inscription dated 1886, front flyleaf.

Contains black-and-white illustration signed "K.G.," p. 197.

405. Ewing, Juliana Horatia

BROTHERS | OF | PITY | AND OTHER TALES OF | BEASTS AND MEN | BY | JULIANA HORATIA EWING | AUTHOR OF "MRS. OVERTHEWAY'S REMEMBRANCES," "A FLAT IRON FOR A | FARTHING," "A WEEK SPENT IN A GLASS POND," &c. &c. | PUBLISHED UNDER THE DIRECTION OF | THE COMMITTEE OF GENERAL LITERATURE AND EDUCATION | APPOINTED BY THE SOCIETY FOR PROMOTING | CHRISTIAN KNOWLEDGE | London | SOCIETY FOR PROMOTING CHRISTIAN KNOWLEDGE, | NORTHUMBERLAND AVENUE, CHARING CROSS: | 43, QUEEN VICTORIA STREET: 48, PICCADILLY | AND 135, NORTH STREET, BRIGHTON | NEW YORK E. & J. B. YOUNG & CO.

[ix] x [xi–xii] [1] 2–199 [200] [1] 2–12 p. 18.0 cm.

Gray cloth. *Front cover:* same as item 404. *Spine:* same as item 404. *Back cover:* same as item 404. White endpapers. Thickness of volume excluding covers: 2.0 cm.

"Printed by Ballantyne, Hanson and Co., London and Edinburgh," p. 199.

"Publications of the Society for Promoting Christian Knowledge," pp. [1] 2–12 at end.

"Depositories: London: Northumberland Avenue, Charing Cross, W.C., 43, Queen Victoria Street, E.C.; 48, Piccadilly, W.; Brighton: 135, North Street," p. 12 at end.

Contains black-and-white illustration signed "K.G.," p. 197.

406. Ewing, Juliana Horatia

BROTHERS | OF | PITY | AND OTHER TALES OF | BEASTS AND MEN | BY THE LATE | JULIANA HORATIA EWING |

AUTHOR OF "JACKANAPES," "OLD-FASHIONED FAIRY TALES," ETC. ETC. | EIGHTEENTH THOUSAND | PUBLISHED UNDER THE DIRECTION OF | THE COMMITTEE OF GENERAL LITERATURE AND EDUCATION | APPOINTED BY THE SOCIETY FOR PROMOTING | CHRISTIAN KNOWLEDGE | LONDON: | Society for Promoting Christian Knowledge, | NORTHUMBERLAND AVENUE, CHARING CROSS, W.C. | 97 WESTBOURNE GROVE, W.; 43 QUEEN VICTORIA STREET, E.C. | BRIGHTON: 135 NORTH STREET. | NEW YORK: E. & J. B. YOUNG & CO. | 1890

[ix] x [xi–xii] [1] 2–199 [200] [1] 2–12 p. 18.2 cm.

Red cloth. *Front cover:* same as item 404. *Spine:* same as item 404. *Back cover:* same as item 404. Gray and white floral endpapers. Thickness of volume excluding covers: 1.5 cm.

"Works by the same author" and "London: Society for Promoting Christian Knowledge, Northumberland Avenue, W.C.," p. [200].

"Publications of the Society for Promoting Christian Knowledge," pp. [1] 2–12, at end.

"Depositories. London: Northumberland Avenue, Charing Cross, S.W.; 97 Westbourne Grove, W.; 43 Queen Victoria Street, E.C.; Brighton: 135 North Street," p. 12 at end.

Inscription dated "Dec. 1893," p. [i].

Contains black-and-white illustration signed "K.G.," p. 197.

407. Geburtstagsbuch | Für unsere Kleinen. | Mit Illustrationen von | Kate Greenaway, Kate Coleman und Anderen. | München: | Theodor Stroefer's Kunstverlag.

[ii] [1] 2–289 [290–96] p. 11.9 cm.

Cream-colored cloth, beveled edges. *Front cover:* Geburtstagsbuch | Für unsere Kleinen. | Illustrirt von | Kate Greenaway & And., stamped in red; picture of three children picking flowers in a rectangular frame, surrounded by flowers and leaves, stamped in red and black. *Spine:* Geburtstags | Buch | Für unsere | Kleinen. | Theo. Stroefer, stamped in red; design of flowers and leaves, stamped in red and black. *Back cover:* circular design in center of young boy and flowers and double-line border, stamped in black. White endpapers.

Inscription dated "Wiesbaden, 1884," front flyleaf.

"Verzeichniss gediegener, edlen Geschmack fördernder Bilderbücher aus Theo. Stroefer's Kunstverlag in München," pp. 283–[96].

Contains the bookplate of Helen H. Wingate.

German translation of Frederick E. Weatherly's *Illustrated Children's Birthday-Book.*

408. Greaves, Annie

    The | Birthday Bouquet | WITH | DAILY QUOTATIONS IN-
TRODUCING | FLOWERS AND NAMES | SELECTED AND
ARRANGED BY | ANNIE GREAVES | [Three-line quotation] |
LONDON | FREDERICK WARNE AND CO. | AND NEW YORK
    [6] 7–287 [288] p. 12.4 cm.

    Olive green moiré cloth. *Front cover:* THE | BIRTHDAY
BOUQUET, stamped in gold on white cloth onlay; author's
monogram and art nouveau design, stamped in gold. *Spine:*
white cloth; THE | BIRTHDAY | BOUQUET, stamped in gold; art
nouveau design and publisher's monogram, stamped in gold.
Back cover: blank. All edges gilt.

    "Printed by Ballantyne, Hanson & Co., at the Ballantyne
Press," pp. [4] and [288].

    Contains twelve unsigned black-and-white illustrations by
K.G., one at the beginning of each month.

    First advertised in *Publisher's Weekly,* September 26, 1903.

    a. Marbled endpapers.

    Contains colored frontispiece signed "K.G." of two young
girls dancing.

    Presented by the Friends of the Detroit Public Library.

    b. Ornamental light orange and white endpapers incorporat-
ing publisher's monogram.

    Contains colored frontispiece signed "K.G." of mother and
child.

    Presented by the Friends of the Detroit Public Library.

409.* Greenaway, Kate

    SMATT FOLK. | Bilder från Barnaverlden | AF | KATE
GREENAWAY. | STOCKHOLM | ALBERT BONNIERS FÖR-
LAG | 1882. | Chr. J. Cato, Köpenhamn.

    [1] l. 2–5 p. 6–28 l. 22.6 cm.

    Brown pictorial boards. *Front cover:* SMATT FOLK. | Bilder
från Barnaverlden | AF | KATE GREENAWAY. | STOCKHOLM |
ALBERT BONNIERS FÖRLAG | 1882., printed in black; picture
of six small children standing in a row holding hands and two
children seated, printed in colors. *Spine:* red cloth. *Back cover:*
circle in center containing picture of young girl in long dress,
bonnet, and fan in hand, printed in colors. Gray endpapers.

    Tan dust wrapper with title, place, publisher, a poem, illus-
tration, and "Pris: 2:75" on front; publisher's advertisement on
back.

*Illustrated.

SMÅTT FOLK.

Bilder från Barnaverlden

AF

KATE GREENAWAY.

STOCKHOLM
ALBERT·BONNIERṢ FÖRLAG
1882.

409. Title page, Scandinavian edition of selections from *Under the Window*.

Beginning with page six the printing is only on the recto of each leaf; verso blank.

Scandinavian edition of selections from *Under the Window.*

410. Harte, Bret

THE QUEEN | OF | THE PIRATE ISLE | BY | BRET HARTE | ILLUSTRATED BY KATE GREENAWAY | ENGRAVED AND PRINTED BY EDMUND EVANS | LONDON | FREDERICK WARNE AND CO. | AND NEW YORK

[9] 10–58 p. 21.7 cm.

Beige cloth. *Front cover:* The Queen | OF THE | Pirate Isle | BY | BRET HARTE | ILLUSTRATED | BY | KATE GREENAWAY, stamped in gold and black; picture of three children on a "Boat" (illustration from p. 16), stamped in colors; double-line border, stamped in gold. *Spine:* blue cloth. *Back cover:* blank. Brown endpapers.

Presented by James C. Dance, Trinity Circle, and June Eckmeter in memory of Bernadine Baker.

411. LITTLE | Boy | BLUE | A COLLECTION OF | NURSERY RHYMES | WITH PICTURES | MARCUS WARD & CO LIMITED | LONDON BELFAST & NEW YORK

[5] 6–32 p. 21.5 cm.

Dark blue glazed pictorial boards. *Front cover:* LITTLE | Boy | BLUE | MARCUS WARD & CO LIMITED, printed in white, light blue, and brown; picture of Little Boy Blue blowing a large horn, printed in colors. *Spine:* dark blue cloth. *Back cover:* same picture of Little Boy Blue, printed in colors. Blue and white floral endpapers.

"Printed and published by Marcus Ward & Co. Limited, London, Belfast, New York," p. [4] (verso of title page).

Contains the bookplate of Helen H. Wingate.

Contains unsigned illustrations by K.G., printed in colors, pp. [3] (title page), 11, 17, and 24.

412. Little Folks: A Magazine for the Young. New and Enlarged Series. London, Paris & New York, Cassell, Petter, Galpin & Co., Vols. 11–12, 1880.

Marbled boards.

Contains black-and-white illustrations signed "K.G.," Vol. 11, pp. 24, 25, 80, 144, 184, and Vol. 12, p. 112, and unsigned black-and-white illustrations by K.G., Vol. 11, pp. 232 and 233.

413. Little Folks: A Magazine for the Young. New and Enlarged Series. London, Paris & New York, Cassell, Petter, Galpin &

Co., Vols. 13–14, 1881.

Blue cloth.

Contains black-and-white illustrations by K.G., p. 57.

414. Yonge, Charlotte

HEARTSEASE | OR | THE BROTHER'S WIFE | ILLUS-
TRATED BY KATE GREENAWAY | London | MACMILLAN
AND CO. | 1882 | The Right of Translation is Reserved

[xii] [1] 2–548 p. 18.0 cm.

Olive green cloth. *Front cover:* two bands, stamped in gold and
black. *Spine:* CHARLOTTE M. | YONGE | HEARTSEASE |
MACMILLAN | & CO., stamped in gold; bands continued from
front cover, stamped in gold and black. *Back cover:* bands continued from front cover, blind-stamped. Black endpapers.

"Novels by Charlotte M. Yonge, Macmillan & Co.," p. [i].

"Novels by Charlotte M. Yonge. Volume II Heartsease. London, Macmillan and Co., 1882," p. [iii].

Contains the bookplate of W. M. and F. B. Collier.

The illustration listed in "List of Illustrations" as being at p.
198 is actually used as the frontispiece. The other two illustrations are inserted after pp. 126 and 224.

INDEX

The numbers given are those of items in this catalogue.

Susan Ruth Thomson, former librarian at the Rare Book Room, Detroit Public Library, received the M.L.S. degree from The University of Michigan.

The manuscript was edited by Jean Owen. The book was designed by Richard Kinney. The display face and text face is Palatino, designed by Hermann Zapf.

The book is printed on Mohawk's Superfine text paper. Manufactured in the United States of America.